J. M. Zunde
BA (Hons), MA, RIBA, Hon MBIAT

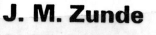

Design procedures
Level 4

Illustrated by Peter Zunde RIBA

Sheffield Hallam University Press
Learning Centre
City Campus
Sheffield S1 1WB

Visit our website: www.shu.ac.uk/shupress/

© Sheffield Hallam University 1989
ISBN 0 86339 203 2

Sheffield Hallam University

First published by
Longman Group Limited 1982

Republished 1989
by PAVIC Publications,
Sheffield Hallam University
with kind permission of
Longman Group Limited

© J M Zunde

ISBN No 086 339 2024

Contents

Preface

As part of his specialised education, the architectural technician is required to obtain a sound knowledge of the process through which a design is developed. He must undertake Unit U77/440, Design Procedures IV as part of the Technician Education Council programme at Higher Certificate or Diploma level in Building Studies.

This book has been closely designed to cover the syllabus of TEC U77/440 in a logical and comprehensive way. It is illustrated by 132 relevant black-and-white drawings. The majority of the topics are related to the development of a simple architectural project, and the student is taken beyond the level of work on which he is likely to be engaged, so as to obtain some understanding of the procedures of all the members of the design team and the reasons for their adoption.

As a detailed explanation of those activities, the book is likely to appeal to a wide range of students and practitioners in design disciplines.

It is assumed that students will be basically numerate and will have background knowledge of Construction Technology up to the level of Construction Technology AIII or BIII (TEC U75/075 or 076).

The author must express warm appreciation of the encouragement and meticulous supervision given by Colin Bassett as General Editor – Building and Civil Engineering – to the Longman Technician Series, and of the assistance and tolerance offered by staff of the publisher's office.

The book could not have been written without the generations of students in whose company she has developed her approach to the subject, and she also acknowledges the valuable help of colleagues, including in particular Keith Slater and Bob O'Hara, who read and made constructive comments upon Chapters 12 and 13 respectively.

Joan Zunde
Sheffield
1981

Chapter 1

The design team in building

The design team

Design is a specialised form of decision-making.

We all take decisions constantly, during every moment of our conscious life – what to wear, what to eat, whether to work or rest – and even when our choices affect no one but ourselves we may be aware of the responsibility decision-making involves. Every choice made will limit the options open at a later stage: we are committing ourselves to a particular route forward, which necessarily excludes others, at every step.

If the individual allowed himself to be aware of the detailed consequences of this multitude of decisions, his sanity would be in peril. Even the greatest chessmasters, playing the game which above all epitomises decision-making, can think only a limited number of moves ahead. He has to be appreciative, though, on the basis of study and experience, of the results likely to flow from his choice of strategy.

In all spheres we must consider the direction in which all our major decisions will take us and others, and in what ways we are committed and limited by them. In particular, it is an essential characteristic of design decisions that they have far-reaching consequences of which it is the designer's duty to be aware. Cost limits affect choice of material, choice of material affects construction method, which in turn affects the overall form of the artefact. Notions of aesthetics have a pervasive effect. This is all true enough of the craftsman developing his ideas during the creative process: every cut made on wood immediately limits the options available at the next stage.

Even more, in cases where the design process is divorced from the execution of the work, full consideration of the results which are consequent on every decision taken is obviously of the first importance. Clearly this is even more vital where, as in the case of building design, the process is one which cannot fall within the purview of an individual but must be carried out by a team of specialists, each of whom has a limited sphere of responsibility.

Each member of such a design team must appreciate the place of his own contribution and its influence on the whole – he must also understand and respect the contributions made by his associates in the team. Naturally, each is aware of the logical basis of his own choices, and can assess how critical or flexible the recommendations based on them can be. It is harder for him to understand how vital the far-reaching requirements spelled out by one of his colleagues may be: he will always be tempted to believe that his own sphere is of greater importance than the others.

For this reason it is essential that the team should have a leader who will listen with respect to the ideas of all the specialists, and in the last analysis will decide where the priorities lie and what compromises should be made, and will see the total effect of the corporate design. A number of different specialists may at varying times lay claim to this role; where structure forms an important part of the design (of bridges, perhaps) the civil engineer will be an appropriate leader: where a whole district is under consideration, the responsibility may sensibly be given to the town planner, and so on. It is usual in the vast majority of cases of building design for the architect to undertake the function. Traditionally, he is the specialist who has been trained to see the total picture, he has had a more stringent training in design than his colleagues, and his education has included sufficient insight into the methods and objectives of his colleagues to allow him to give proper weight to their recommendations. It is indeed true that the profession of architecture has evolved specifically to provide someone fitted to undertake this key role.

It is a mistake to think of the architect as an omniscient person who knows all about every aspect of building design and construction, yet specialists frequently find it cause for criticism when they discover gaps in the architect's knowledge of their own territory. Each specialist should be aware that he has a deeper insight into his own particular area of expertise than the team leader: this should not surprise him. The special contribution of the architect is his ability to take an overview, to see the problem as a whole, and to weld the contributions of the specialists into a coherent entity (Fig. 1.1).

The architect

The lengthy training of the architect to fit him for this very onerous, challenging (and enjoyable) task has traditionally been based on design

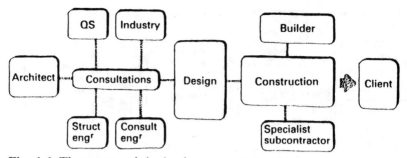

Fig. 1.1 The team and the leader

exercises, so that his special skills in the analysis of design problems and the integration of solutions to them are highly developed. As he progresses at the school of architecture, through a programme of carefully graded exercises, the knowledge needed for their solution, whether it lies in the technical, sociological, economic, aesthetic or some other field, is slotted into his curriculum. He is, above all, trained to see the relationships between these various areas of knowledge.

Once trained, if he is to use the title 'architect', the professional must submit himself to a stringent code of conduct, which controls the ways in which he can operate professionally in the interests of the client, the public, and the profession as a whole. In particular, he must take great care to divorce his decisions from commercial pressures of any kind.

Architects frequently find that they become specialists in one or another particular kind of building, perhaps because of being employed by an authority whose building programme is limited to a particular building type, or because a reputation based on early success leads to further analogous commissions. Though this may have the advantage that they have a wealth of accumulated relevant information at their finger tips, it may have associated disadvantages. The person concerned could find it harder to think creatively in each new case, and may tend to repeat tried solutions. There can be an advantage to client and designer in a change of scene from time to time (Fig. 1.2).

The structural engineer

The basic education of the structural engineer is frequently that of a civil engineer, with special emphasis on the understanding of forces and their effects upon materials. It includes a rigorous training in the analysis of structures, and a comprehensive understanding of the whole scientific basis of the ways in which materials and structures behave.

He is able, as a result of this training, not only to apply certain well understood formulae to standard cases, but more importantly to look at the non-standard case with understanding. While some engineers may tend to concentrate on timber, or steel or perhaps prestressed structures, the underlying principles in each case will remain the same, and we should be able to look to the engineer at the

4

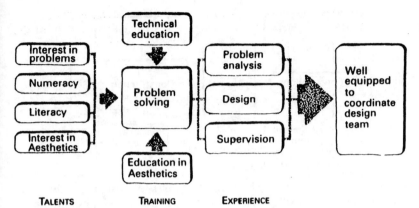

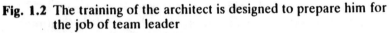

TALENTS   TRAINING   EXPERIENCE

Fig. 1.2 The training of the architect is designed to prepare him for the job of team leader

early design stage for an assessment of the implications of the choice of various constructional systems.

The mechanical engineer

The concern of this specialist is in essence with those functions of a building that are best fulfilled by mechanical contrivances – boilers for heating, escalators for transport, for example. Because of his developed ability to devise suitable equipment for such purposes, he has acquired the additional role of designing distribution services, too, even when no mechanical means of distribution are involved. Indeed, some mechanical engineers have so diversified into the realm of drainage and plumbing design, for example, that they should really take the new title of 'Services Engineers'.

  The training, however, is concerned with the assessment of needs (in areas such as heating, for example) calculation of the optimum means of satisfying such needs, and design of suitable systems to perform the function. Very often they choose the mechanical devices needed from manufacturers' ranges, rather than designing them from scratch, in the building sphere.

  It is quite common, with no disrespect to the engineer, for the architect to find it necessary to vary the engineer's proposals to take account of aspects of the problem of which the specialist could hardly be expected to be aware.

The electrical engineer

Understanding of the workings and use of electricity is of course at the core of this engineer's expertise. He finds that electricity in building is largely used for illumination, and he has therefore to understand the principles of lighting and the levels required for different purposes. Where power supply is concerned, he must be well aware of safety requirements and optimum loadings.

Like the mechanical engineer, with whom he frequently finds himself in close cooperation, he may tend to see his own aspects of the design problem in isolation, and will need to be helped to see how his ideas must integrate with those of his colleagues.

The landscape architect

This specialist's design training is of a very similar kind to that of the architect, but with the emphasis naturally on the use of pavings, boundary structures and plant material. His contribution should not be grafted on to the end of the design phase, when all the decisions affecting the form of the building have been taken, but should be related to the development of the building design at every step.

The interior designer

Interior design must always be regarded as an integral part of the design of a total building, and many architects will wish to undertake all work in this area themselves. If a specialist IS to be employed (perhaps because of the importance from a marketing point of view of the interiors of a hotel, or for some other good reason) he will preferably be a person who has specialised on the basis of at least a partial training in architecture, and who therefore understands the principles of design as they are understood by an architect. He should see the interiors as an aspect of a whole, and not as 'stage sets' – and he should be brought into the discussions from the outset.

The quantity surveyor

The professionally trained quantity surveyor has an unequalled knowledge and understanding of the intricate forces which affect the cost of buildings, which is invaluable to the design team provided it is available as required. He should, for this reason, be a member of that team, so that he can constantly monitor the economic effect of potential choices, and cost can be given due weight in arriving at decisions. He should not, of course, ever be in danger of becoming a minatory figure always insisting that the cheapest option must be adopted.

Design team meetings

All of the professionals referred to above need to be aware of the ways in which each others' minds are working, throughout design. None can effectively work in isolation, and any attempt on the part of any individual to do so will have deleterious effects on the total result of their collective labours. Rather than communicating through the architect, they will generally find mutual benefit in regular semi-formal meetings of the team, when progress can be monitored and difficulties ventilated.

There will generally have been an agreed programme of work for the design stage of the project, which may well have been expressed

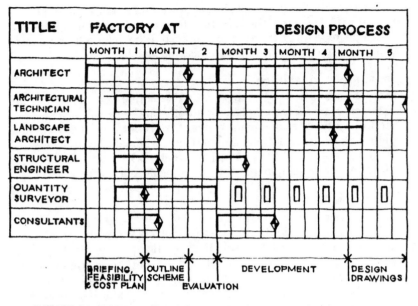

TITLE	FACTORY AT				DESIGN PROCESS	
	MONTH 1	MONTH 2	MONTH 3	MONTH 4	MONTH 5	
ARCHITECT						
ARCHITECTURAL TECHNICIAN						
LANDSCAPE ARCHITECT						
STRUCTURAL ENGINEER						
QUANTITY SURVEYOR						
CONSULTANTS						

BRIEFING, FEASIBILITY & COST PLAN | OUTLINE SCHEME | EVALUATION | DEVELOPMENT | DESIGN DRAWINGS

CUTOFF DATES BY WHICH FIRM DECISIONS
MUST BE REACHED ARE SHOWN ◈

Fig. 1.3 The bar chart is one graphic way of monitoring progress on
the design

as a bar chart (Fig. 1.3). It is essential that the critical points at which
members of the team are dependent on one anothers' progress are
clearly known, if smooth progress is to be made, and that any
likelihood of delay should be identified well in advance.

The choice of members of a design team who will share a common
philosophy and be able to work together compatibly, has been said to
be one of the most important contributory factors to the success of a
building project.

External contacts of the design team

The contractor

The builder possesses an important body of specialised knowledge
which it is highly desirable should be available during design, yet
where the common forms of contract are adopted this expertise is
difficult to tap. Alternative contract patterns to overcome this
difficulty are more and more often being adopted, and the variations
due to some of them are discussed later in this chapter.

Care has to be taken to differentiate between the special detailed
knowledge of technology (and especially the methods most

conveniently available to his firm) of the contractor, and purely commercial considerations. Each of the professionals referred to above is motivated by the aim of finding the optimum solution to a problem posed by the client, putting this above any consideration of the profitability of the operation. A contractor who is in business must quite properly put his return to his shareholders high on his list of priorities.

This is not to impute irresponsibility to him; it is to point out an indisputable and often overlooked fact. The point may be particularly relevant where subcontract tenders are obtained on a design-and-install basis. It is quite common for heating or electrical schemes to be obtained in this way rather than to have schemes prepared by disinterested professionals who will advise between alternatives in a particular case. This works well in a very large number of cases, but it is important that the design team bears in mind the point spelled out in the preceding paragraph.

The client

It should not be necessary for the members of the design team, corporately or individually, to meet the client or his representative. For the client to be represented (other than by the architect, who is, in fact, his agent for the work) during the deliberations of the designers can have the unfortunate effect of encouraging him to rethink his requirements, change the conditions of the problem and cause large quantities of abortive work. The architect will normally obtain the detailed information which transforms the first bald commission into a 'brief' on which design work can be based, and if this is efficiently done it should not be necessary to seek further information or discussion from the client until he is asked to react to a detailed scheme.

A proposed system, whereby the client employs a 'building officer' who undertakes part of the function of the architect so far as briefing and the convening of design meetings is concerned, is discussed later. Such an arrangement is rare and the advantages claimed for it are yet to be established as automatic.

The technician

All of the professionals in the design team may be backed-up by their own team of tracers, clerical staff and, of course, technicians. This is particularly likely to be true in the case of the architect, because the commitment from his office is likely to exceed (in man hours) that of the other specialists concerned, and the team he must devote to the project will necessarily be larger.

The Royal Institute of British Architects (RIBA) and Society of Architectural and Associated Technicians (SAAT) see the role of the technician as:
1. Collection and analysis of technical data.

2. Making working-drawings for use on site, and presentation drawings for clients.
3. Contract administration.
4. Land and building survey work.
5. Attendance at site meetings and organisation of work schedules.
6. Inspections of work.
7. Collection of information on the performance of finished buildings.
8. Office management.
9. Liaison with specialist advisers.

In the design period this is likely to involve the technician in considerable research, and in the presentation of the results of his investigations in forms which make drawing conclusions from the data on its implications an easy matter. If he is to carry out this task effectively it is essential that he should understand the reasons for which the information is required and the kinds of decisions that may be influenced by it. He must also be clearly aware of the necessity for relevant information to be available at a particular time.

A second important part of his function at design stage is likely to be concerned with the presentation of the proposed solution to the client (and perhaps to the public through the press) in terms in which it will be readily and correctly understood. For this he will need to apply all his understanding of communication theory, and his skill in employing appropriate communication methods.

The process of design

The development of a scheme from the first hint of a potential

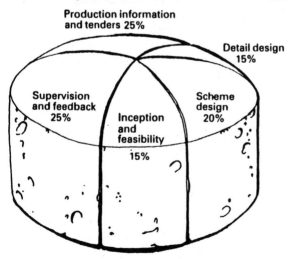

Fig. 1.4 Half the total architects' fees are for the design work

commission through to the presentation of a design forms stages A–D of the RIBA 'Stages of Work', and are assumed by the RIBA to account for 35 per cent of the total fees for the job (Fig. 1.4).

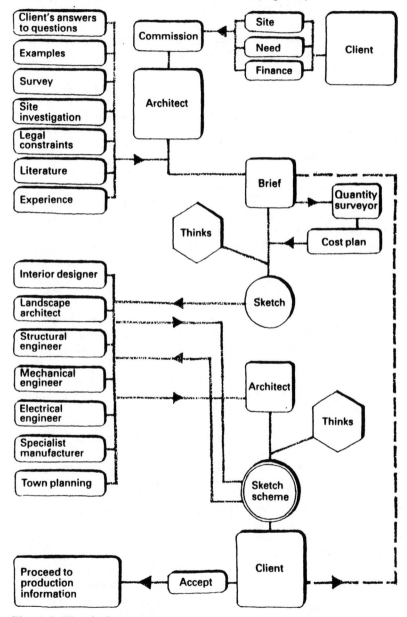

Fig. 1.5 The design process

The client approaches an architect with a need (whether that is a need to provide accommodation for his own use, or a desire for a profitable investment in lettable space or saleable houses) a site, and a source of finance. It is not an architect's responsibility to deal in or discover potential sites or to seek out sources of money, and neither should he be expected to divine the needs of the client (though he has, of course, to employ considerable skill in assisting the client to analyse and express those needs).

Figure 1.5 shows how the process is likely to develop.

The first step is the collection of information from a variety of sources (this is gone into in detail in Ch. 3) to transform the commission (which may be a very simple document) into the mass of material that will form the 'brief' upon which the design will be based.

While this material is being collected – and perhaps when little is available beyond a knowledge of the size of the building anticipated, the cost limits, and the immediately visible characteristics of the proposed site – a feasibility study may be needed. This will assure everyone concerned of the viability of the scheme as outlined. There will, of course, be constant reference back throughout the later development of the project to ensure that this viability has not been eroded.

Once this stage has been satisfactorily concluded, no time should be lost in identifying and appointing the consultant specialists whose help will be needed with the scheme. Not all of the persons listed above will, naturally, be employed on every project. However, all those who are in fact required should be given the advantage of being brought into the discussions at the earliest possible stage, when they can make their most useful contributions.

At their first meeting, the members of the team will normally discuss general questions, such as their response to particular restraints imposed by the nature of the site, the availability of services, or the need for stringent economy, etc. They will agree to present recommendations on such matters for discussion by the team, so that a common policy is formulated, understood and adopted. It is essential that there is a clear understanding that decisions are to be taken in a logical order, and that once taken thoughtfully by the team as a whole, they are to be accepted along with all the consequences that may flow from them. Another function of the initial meeting will be to agree the working programme (as referred to in Fig. 1.3 above).

The parts of the design will evolve through a series of controlled stages, as is described in detail in Chapter 8. The biggest and most far-reaching decisions must be the first to be taken, while discussions will culminate with the more detailed ones. At every stage there will be discussion, based on appreciation of the consequences of alternative strategies, and each specialist will urge his point of view, but all must accept the position of the architect as final arbiter if consensus cannot be reached. Each decision, once taken, must be accepted by all.

During the whole of this process there will naturally be constant reference back to the detailed brief to ensure that its requirements and assessment of priorities are being adhered to.

Eventually, with little rethinking or abortive effort, a developed scheme will emerge from this logical process. This will satisfy the team of designers as a proper response to the problem as defined to them.

It now remains to convince the client.

Presentation drawings are required, to explain the scheme, its relationship to its surroundings and its advantages – and not to conceal any points at which the inevitable compromises have been made.

It is always to be hoped that the client's reaction will be positive or even enthusiastic. If this is not the case, some re-examination may be needed. Do the drawings present their intentions so that these are being correctly understood? Has some implicit requirement of the client been ignored because he thought it so obvious as not to need expression? (He might, for example, think it quite unnecessary to express dislike of a particular style of window, if it seemed to him quite clear that all right-thinking people would share his prejudice!) On the other hand, has the client changed his mind?

It should be possible for a rejected design to be the result only of this last situation, if the process of design has been logically and conscientiously carried out. If this should be the case, it should be made clear that tinkering with the finished design is unlikely to provide a satisfactory end-result, but that (depending on the extent to which the change is basic – the point at which the decision was taken) it is necessary to return to an early point in the development of the design so that the consequences of the changed condition are fully accounted for.

For example, if the client now expresses a wish for accommodation planned at upper-floor level to be arranged on the ground floor, this will clearly affect very early design decisions, and work must recommence from a very early stage. On the other hand, if the change has to do with a less crucial point, such as the nature of floor coverings, less work may have to be abandoned. It should always be possible to tell from the bar-chart (Fig. 1.3) at what point the critical decision was taken, and therefore from what point the design team must retrace its steps.

If the brief has, in effect, been changed there will naturally be duplicate fees to be charged for this extra work – a point of which the client must be made fully aware. This underlines the vital importance of comprehensive briefing at the proper time.

Provided the scheme is accepted, however, the programme moves forward to detailing stage. The design decisions now to be taken are of a much more superficial character, and no decisions previously arrived at are to be upset. Production drawings are made, beginning with those at the largest scale and gradually reducing the detail and the scale until the small-scale site plan is the last to be produced.

This process of implementing the design, however, lies outside the scope of this book.

Fee management contract

With the method of working so far outlined in this chapter, which is based on the assumption that the Joint Contracts Tribunal Contracts will be used, no thought is given to appointment of a contractor (or very often, any subcontractors) until all the design decisions have been taken. Though it may be true that subcontractors are appointed for major portions of the work before the main contract is let – and this can be a very helpful procedure in eliminating areas of doubt and provisional measurements and sums from the Bill of Quantities – these subcontractors themselves would still be appointed too late to influence the design of their own particular work, or work affected by it.

To take advantage of the builder's expertise at the design stage, one strategy sometimes adopted is the use of a 'Fee Management' contract. A builder who is active in the normal commercial hurly burly of the industry is selected and appointed at the same stage as the other consultants, to take a quasi-professional role. He will not himself stand to make profit or loss out of the contract, but will be remunerated by percentage fee, and the whole of the building work will be done, under

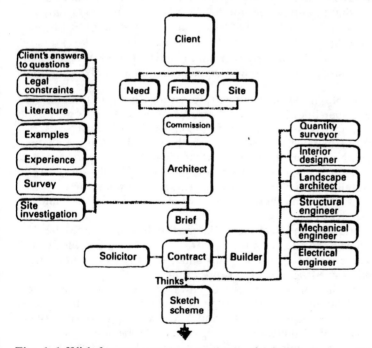

Fig. 1.6 With fee management contracts the builder's expertise is available during the design process

his organisation and management, by subcontractors. He will, however, be able to influence choices of materials, methods of construction and the plan form in exactly the same way as other members of the design team, and may so have a far-reaching effect on the efficiency of the building operation. It is claimed that greater savings than the cost of the additional fee are to be expected where this system is adopted (see Fig. 1.6).

Direct labour

Attempts have also been made to obtain similar advantages by having the architect (or a trained building manager on his staff) act as general contractor and take day-to-day control of the building operation. The advantages in the efficient use of labour and materials are less clear than with fee management, but such a system undoubtedly makes the architect think clearly about the way in which his ideas are to be executed (see Fig. 1.7).

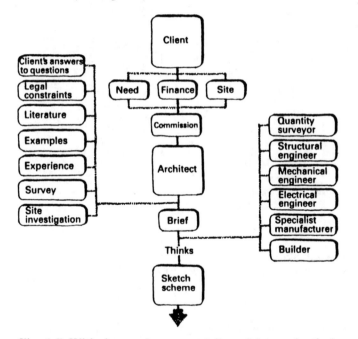

Fig. 1.7 With the employment of direct labour, the designer can have immediate control over all the specialist constructors

Package deal

The package deal firms aim to make economies by eradicating the design team as a separate entity (though, of course, design work still has to be done and paid for). They claim considerable savings, but it would seem that their system only works well where 'off the peg' buildings on simple sites are needed. The design process in many such cases seems to consist largely of modification of one of a limited series of standard designs to meet any particular conditions. There is no doubt that there is a market for buildings of this kind, and standardised houses and workshops satisfy a very large number of users.

There will always be the need, however, for the greater efficiency of the tailor-made job, and it seems unlikely that the package dealer (to whom, quite fairly, commercial considerations are all important) will be able to satisfy it (Fig. 1.8).

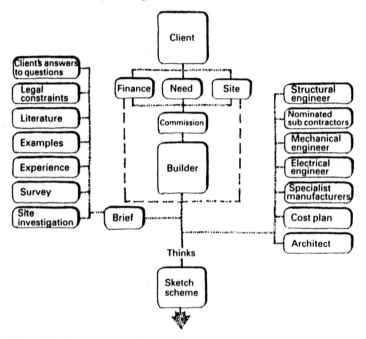

Fig. 1.8 In a package deal contract the architect gives up his coordinating and supervisory roles to the builder

Building consultant

The appointment by a client of a 'Building Consultant' to coordinate a project seems on the surface very attractive. Whether such a person was a salaried member of the client's organisation, or an outside professional remunerated by fee, he could provide a useful service. On the one hand, he might coordinate and schedule the requirements of the client, and his knowledge of building should be sufficient for him to ask the right questions and make a sound assessment of priorities and relevance. On the other hand, he should have the experience to bring together a compatible team of specialists and coordinate their work. At all times, he should act as channel of communication between client and designers. He has, later, the further functions of selecting firms to be invited to tender and eventually taking over the building on the client's behalf.

The necessary background of training and experience for such an individual seems at present to be undefined, though it will be patent that he is largely performing tasks traditionally undertaken by the architect. These are tasks which many architects are said to resent because they obstruct their freedom to get on with the primary task of design.

There are perhaps some architects who already perform almost exactly in the way described, delegating what some of their colleagues would think of as design responsibility to their staffs. Defining the interface between the functions of architect and building consultant could present difficulty. It is a matter, basically, of establishing who carries the professional responsibility for the results of decisions, and is paid accordingly.

The system is not sufficiently common yet in the UK for any clear idea to have emerged as to how it might develop and what success it may attain. Nor can it be evident what popularity from clients and architects it can expect (see Fig. 1.9).

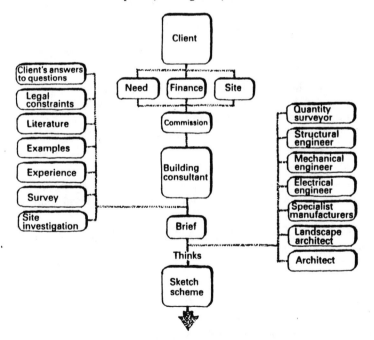

Fig. 1.9 The building consultant would take over the architect's coordinating role, but leave open tendering as an option

Chapter 2

Design methodology

The aspects of design to be considered

There are three aspects to any design which, though closely related, can be seen to be distinct.

1. Satisfaction of the functional demands of the problem.
2. Development of appropriate technical methods of embodying the solution in a straightforward and logical manner.
3. Proper application of the rules of aesthetics to produce an artefact which is enjoyable to use and to see.

No design solution can be considered satisfactory which fails to provide an adequate answer to the problem as posed in each of these three areas – and provide these answers in an integrated, logical and readily understood manner.

In Architecture as in all other Operative Arts, the end must direct the Operation. The end is to build well.
Well building hath three Conditions, Commodity, Firmness and Delight!

(Sir Henry Wotton, *Elements of Architecture*, 1624)

Figure 2.1 shows this graphically.
In the case of even the simplest design exercise, functional considerations will include understanding of the way in which the object is intended to be used (as well as the ways in which it may be adapted or even misused) and also the proper deployment

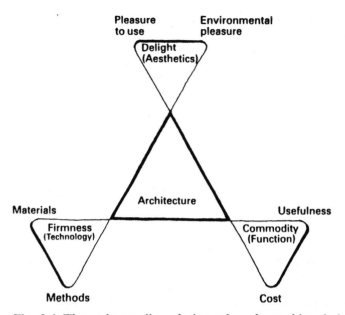

Pleasure
to use

Environmental
pleasure

Materials

Architecture

Usefulness

Methods

Cost

Fig. 2.1 The truly excellent design solves the problem in terms of
technology, function and aesthetics

of the resources of time, labour, materials and money which may be
available. Technological aspects not only take into account the choice
of the most suitable material for a specific purpose, but also the
understanding and the adoption of the most advantageous method of
manufacture, assembly or construction. In the aesthetic field, the
designer must be concerned not only with the pleasure afforded to the
onlooker but also with the satisfaction of the owner and users.

Where buildings are concerned, it is possible to be more specific,
and say that functional satisfaction must be based on analysis of the
processes (whether these are human, organisational or mechanical) the
building is intended to house, in the light of the imposed cost limits
and taking into account constraints arising from the proposed site and
the speed with which the building is required.

Technologically, the designer must be aware of the materials and
systems that the industry can offer him at that time and in that place,
and the constraints that may be imposed by any selection he might
make.

Aesthetically, he must consider the building both as a background
to the processes it will contain and also as an incident in the townscape
which will affect the daily lives of a large population.

Integration of these areas is a task for a skilled and experienced
professional: architecture is the result of such integration, and while it
is possible to imagine buildings which torture materials into unnatural
forms or ask them to ape each other, buildings which ignore the

simplest guidelines of aesthetics, or buildings which ignore some basic functional purpose or serve no recognisable purpose at all, these cannot be regarded as architecture. We all know that they exist, and we must recognise that they impoverish the life of the community. The aim of all designers should be to avoid such blots on the townscape.

Function

In Chapter 4 you will find a detailed analysis of the functional constraints likely to apply to buildings – requirements of space and comfort for the occupier, of the relationship between spaces for convenience in use, as well as consideration of the efficient use of resources. In the early part of the present century, the influential architectural 'school' of functionalism was based on the idea that, if a building was designed to perform its function well, good architecture would inevitably result.

Le Corbusier taught us that a house was a 'machine for living in' and suggested that it should be designed on the same lines as any other machine.

Of course, we can now see that the logical conclusion to this train of thought, in a less sensitive mind, is the Nissen hut. Corbusier and the 'internationalists' were instinctively fine designers of great sensitivity, so that they applied aesthetic principles whether they thought about them or not. Functionalism led designers generally away from the idea of camouflaging poor massing with distractingly applied decorations, and produced some remarkably pure pieces of design, but could also be used as an excuse for the perpetration of appallingly ill-considered monstrosities.

Buildings have to serve functional purposes, and the result of ignoring functional criteria is likely to be either a building so unsuitable to its purpose that it is soon abandoned or altered or else a building that causes irritation and fatigue to all its users. In the extreme, the non-functional building is nothing more than a folly or a piece of stage scenery.

Technology

Chapter 5 is concerned with the technical constraints on building. Good building naturally uses suitable materials and methods of construction chosen from among those made available by the building industry, and does so in such a manner that the choice seems automatic and unforced. For this to be done, the designer must be well aware of the vocabulary of structural means from which he can choose, taking into account the relative costs of various materials as well as their capabilities, the availability of skilled labour and the advantages of factory production. He needs to know what plant may be available, even though it is not for him to dictate its use, and the relative costs of skilled and unskilled labour and mechanical means.

This vocabulary, of course, varies in different places and at different times. The skills available in a developing country may be restricted while unskilled labour is relatively abundant. The need to import materials may limit the desirability of choosing them, and so on. It is always necessary to be aware of the whole of the available range of methods: an appropriate choice a generation ago may be rendered invalid today in changed circumstances and by the development of new and more suitable materials, the decline of craftsmanship in a particular trade, or the relative cost of transport.

Whatever materials and methods of assembly are chosen, they must (if satisfactory building is to result) be used in a logical, straightforward and entirely honest manner. Rendered brickwork should not ape reinforced concrete, nor should concrete ape stone. Each material and structural system should be exploited to employ and express its own capabilities, and this will have an important effect on the final appearance of the building.

In the mid-twentieth century, the Brutalists carried this principle to what seemed a logical conclusion. They invited us to regard applied finishes as undesirable and unnecessary – the natural character of materials and services should be expressed, and provided these were properly designed an acceptable and even exciting result could be achieved. The very salutary discipline this point of view exercised on the design of the basic parts of a building could be nothing but beneficial, but it was soon found to be both a more difficult and a more expensive operation than had immediately been apparent. If every electric conduit is to be exposed, not only must its run (and the positions of the clips) be carefully plotted by the architect, but the electrician must be meticulous in following the detail. This is time-consuming. Fairfaced brickwork which is to be exposed needs more care to produce than rough brickwork to be plastered, and so on. Some finishes, too, are needed for practical reasons of acoustics, fire resistance and so on, and cannot be eliminated.

This does not invalidate the basic approach, which is that everything that goes into a building should be carefully thought out and honestly used – and that nothing which serves neither practical nor aesthetic purposes should be included.

The notion that a fine building is simply one that is well built is self-evidently false, yet sound building is an important component of good architecture.

Aesthetics

The vocabulary of visual aesthetics is dealt with in Chapter 7, and this is a science with which everyone concerned with design must have considerable familiarity.

There is an idea about that architects are concerned only with aesthetics – almost with applying a cosmetic façade to a soundly built, functionally laid out building as a kind of afterthought. I was once asked, quite seriously, whether I didn't think architects should be relieved from the task of analysis and coordination, and brought in as consultants once the basic form of the building had been determined, to ensure that it looked pleasant! The questioner apparently expected architects to welcome this as it would release them to concentrate on 'design'.

I trust that my readers will immediately reject such an idea, realising that it is based on a fallacious understanding of the nature of design.

Excellence in building is of course only attained where appearance, soundness of construction and usefulness have been developed hand in hand and in a fully integrated manner.

Understanding of the principles of visual aesthetics – of what makes one shape, one arrangement or one group of objects enjoyable to see and to use and another unpleasant – is not a talent one either has or has not. The eye can be trained to recognise satisfactory design, and the mind to understand the reasons for its success, and the proper use of unity, rhythm and colour, proportion and massing is a skill which can be acquired.

Most people tend to be prejudiced in favour of what is familiar and inclined to be suspicious of what is new, and it takes practice to be able to recognise the good and the bad aspects of both. Alternatively, we sometimes seize what is new and 'modern' for that reason alone – and think we are designing well if our work is fashionable in appearance. This is a splendid way to produce work which will rapidly look dated and tawdry.

Good appearance can rarely, if ever, be grafted on to a design that has been produced without thought of aesthetics. It must emerge from an understanding (which may seem almost subconscious) of good massing, unity, balance and so on which is kept in equilibrium with a grasp of technical practicability while the functional problem is solved.

Integration

The greatest problem in design is preserving this equilibrium. It is easy in hindsight to see that at different historical periods designers have tended to favour one or another of the three aspects at the expense of the others, and much more difficult to understand that one is (almost inevitably) at risk from the same trap oneself.

Houses in the early twentieth century responded to the new freedom in planning made possible by the use of framed structures: the needs of the house were rethought in terms of flows and relationships rather than self-contained boxes, and the revolutionary appearance which resulted caused enormous effort to be expended on an external appearance devoid of stylistic mannerisms carried over from the past.

Such careful and conscious design produced masterpieces, but has also left us an inheritance of mediocre and imitative design, where either the open plan, or the framed structure or the rendered walls of the international style have been adopted as though this were a passport to excellence. It was the care that mattered, and the care had been lost.

Appropriation of gimmicks in the hope of passing off one's work as part of a mainstream of design when one has neither understood the philosophy nor bothered to apply the principles is not only unscrupulous – it is likely to result in rapid unmasking as bogus.

Good design is practically always conscious and careful. Carlyle told us that genius is a transcendent capacity for taking trouble. The notion of the virtuoso designer dashing off a few brilliant sketches is false. The only people who could ever even appear to approach this method would be ones to whom the whole mechanism of design – functional, technical and aesthetic – was so ingrained that it appeared to be innate. The processes of analysis and synthesis might not, in such a case, be evident to an onlooker, but they must be present, none the less.

Of course, there is always the lucky stroke – the 'inspiration' that survives rigorous testing and evaluation, and that because of this may seem to invalidate my argument. Consideration will make clear that such serendipity is not to be relied on – and that, in any case, an object designed in such a fashion could hardly be foisted upon a client without very careful examination AFTER the initial brainwave.

If this is true in the case of a teacup or a chair, consider how much more it must be so in the intricate case of the design of a building.

It is desirable to bear in mind that building design operates at two levels. There are the one-off buildings on important sites which quite evidently have to be analysed in detail and at great length when design begins. Great sums of money are being spent on buildings which may be crucial elements in a townscape, and which will continue to be used for closely specialised purposes for many years. Few would argue that stringent examination of every influence was necessary as the earliest stage of design, in the case of theatres, cathedrals or town halls.

Many buildings, however, form an almost anonymous background to our lives. Houses, factories or offices would be intrusive if their appearance was overemphatic. A case can be made for 'vernacular design' in such cases – indeed, it is possible to predicate a two-tier architectural profession, though most practitioners would prefer to have the opportunity from time to time of designing one of the one-off monuments while learning their craft on a programme of workmanlike but unobtrusive buildings. In the past, vernacular design for routine buildings was the rule, and many of the towns and villages we most admire and seek to preserve are hardly consciously 'designed' at all. Local materials have been used in repetitive ways evolved over centuries by local craftsmen to meet their particular conditions. The unity inevitably produced gives the region the character we admire.

Today we lack such a well understood vernacular of design, to the regret of many. We also have to produce a much wider variety of buildings and meet needs which evolve at greater speeds than was the case in the past. We cannot, therefore, afford the leisurely evolutionary process which produced the Cotswold villages: we have to face a meticulously analysed functional problem with an armoury of well understood and up-to-date technology, and an eye trained in the understanding of aesthetic values.

We can still learn from historical examples, though.

Gothic churches have plans which express the needs of mediaeval rituals but are also closely related to a sophisticated method of construction. The aesthetic effect results in large measure from the unity of the conception and the rhythms imposed by the repetitive construction. Every detail has a practical as well as an aesthetic purpose, as well as being an honest expression of the method of construction adopted.

To design a modern church in imitation of a gothic one would not inevitably result in equal success. The rituals of the Church have changed and a different plan form is more likely to be suitable: reinforced concrete is a more economical, and accessible, material than stone masonry in the late twentieth century, and gargoyles are less likely to be an acceptable method of disposing of rainwater than gutters and drains.

We should, however, attempt to apply the same principles in design.

A well-designed church will still express its function (and satisfy it), it will still use structurally exciting construction and the details of design will spring from practical needs. So we may find a square plan with central altar, the shell concrete roof soaring to a central lunette, and the acoustic break-up of internal surfaces providing decoration – and this building would be more securely part of a tradition of church architecture than any pastiche on the gothic could possibly be.

Theatres provide another area where both the criteria and the methods by which they can be achieved have changed, and are indeed still evolving. A modern theatre is a most sophisticated machine for presenting dramatic performances. It may or may not have a proscenium or an apron stage, there may be a revolve, lifts, a tower. Modern constructional methods, with giant spans, allow every seat to be planned to have a good view – there are no intermediate supports, and the distance from the stage can be limited. Communities expect their theatres, too, to be striking in appearance, but would not accept a beautiful exterior as excuse for an inadequate orchestra pit or poor acoustics.

Because higher standards CAN be achieved than was the case in the eighteenth century, higher practical standards are demanded. Companies and their audiences need to experiment with new theatrical experiences, and require flexibility in their facilities. Of course, all artistic enterprise flourishes on restrictions, and the best performances are not always those given in the most modern theatres. None the less, designers have a duty to exploit the gamut of modern methods to obtain good sight-lines, flexible lighting, good fire escapes – as well as an inviting and attractive appearance.

Fig. 2.2 Traditional forms of drinking-vessels show how a design alters in response to different conditions

The various drinking vessels shown in Fig. 2.2 illustrate, in a simple way, how the considerations of function, technology and aesthetics influence the design of everyday objects. Each of these traditional shapes evolved to satisfy a basically similar but subtly different function.

All exist to convey a quantity of liquid to the human mouth, to be drunk. Why then, should the shapes and materials be so different? Examination shows that in some cases the liquid will be hot, so that a handle is needed. In some cases, the container will be used where there is fine furniture or linen, so that a base or saucer to avoid marking is added. The coffee mug and the tankard are more capacious than the other vessels – but the tankard narrows towards the top to concentrate the head on the beer (and perhaps for stability in conditions where this is critical!) The bottle, of course, is to be used in the inverted position, and has been designed to allow a steady flow of liquid to be controlled by the consumer.

It can be seen, further, that the choice of materials to be used has been made in the light of the functional constraints. The clear glass for wine shows-off colour and clarity, the cut glass for a liqueur emphasises a jewel-like richness. Elegant china for a teacup contrasts with rugged pottery for the mug. The tasteless but indestructible pewter for the tankard and the sterilisable plastic for the baby's bottle are equally practical selections.

This choice having been made, each object has been manufactured in the most straightforward possible manner – blown

glass, sheet metal fabrication, moulded plastic and so on. The shapes
that result are clearly functional as well as easily made. Their good
proportions need only to be enhanced by a minimum of simple applied
decoration, chosen and placed to emphasise the good structural points
of the design.

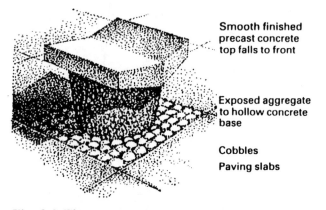

Smooth finished
precast concrete
top falls to front

Exposed aggregate
to hollow concrete
base

Cobbles

Paving slabs

Fig. 2.3 The seat was designed by the application of the techniques
discussed, integrating the demands of function, the chosen
material and the wish for an interesting appearance

The seat shown in Fig. 2.3 was developed consciously, while the
drinking vessels are the result of years of evolution, but similar
processes have been at work. A local authority wished to provide
occasional seats in connection with paved areas in the town centre.
These would be installed from time to time as opportunity arose, and
there was no question of storage space for large numbers of seats. The
seats might be placed singly or in groups, they were intended as
short-term perches rather then long-term places to relax, and they
needed to look urban and sculptural when unoccupied. They should
neither provide a hazard nor attract vandalism.

The first decisions were functional. The seat should be backless to
discourage lengthy occupation, and should be related to the size of a
standard paving-slab so that deployment was easy. It should have two
parallel ends, so that a row of seats would be viable.

Secondly, after consideration of wood and GRP, precast concrete
was chosen as the most suitable material. This was rugged, and likely
to stand up to attempted vandalism, would fit-in with the hard
surroundings (which were already tempered by planting in
concrete containers) and – most important – moulds could be stored
and the seats could be cast as they were required. Concrete seats, too,
could be anchored by reinforcing rods embedded in the concrete.

In determining the shape of the units, a practical consideration was
to have an easily-drained top, so that passers-by were not being invited

to sit in pools of water. The proportions of the top were designed to look robust and to provide a modestly interesting feature in the townscape, and the recessed, drum-shaped base was given a rough, exposed aggregate finish to conform with the cobbles used to pave no-go areas. Finally, the overall shape was made to look well-balanced and proportioned.

Each seat replaces a single paving slab, and is set in cobbles. A row provides elbow room – or the shopping bag can be popped on to the next seat – and the undulating line of a row of seats is an attractive feature. Although the seats were designed in the early sixties (when rugged concrete was, of course, much in vogue) they still look and work satisfactorily today.

Comparison of the houses built by primitive societies, as shown in Fig. 2.4, reveals that the differences in their design can be accounted for in much the same way as the differences in the drinking-vessels discussed above.

Fig. 2.4 The houses vary because of differences in climate and available materials

The igloo, the teepee, the tent and the hut all exist to provide shelter for a family unit, and to use basic human skills. They differ strikingly, however.

The pattern of life in different climates does, of course, vary. How much time can a particular family spend out of doors, what kinds of food have to be prepared, how permanent must the shelter be?

The climate itself makes different demands on the shelter which is to provide protection – (is wind, rain, frost or sun the main hazard?) Then, of course, it is the most readily available local material which has in each case been chosen for construction, and this has in turn imposed constraints based on handling sizes and structural capacity. The shapes, therefore, of a suspended cloth tent for desert conditions, a wicker hut from the jungle, a portable skin-tent, and an ice-house intended to last a bitter winter through, are very different.

Sophisticated modern designers must be ready similarly to respond to changes within the conditions defining the situation in which they operate.

People's demands on buildings continually become more exacting as they see that such demands are capable of fulfilment, and thus the resources of technology are continually stretched. Advocates of alternative technologies who would have us retreat to self-sufficiency base the achievement of their enticing dream on use of sophisticated methods of harnessing windpower, of thermal insulation, or of recycling waste. The levels of thermal insulation commonly demanded today could only be achieved by the application of modern materials, the levels of daylighting often asked for require large openings only modern structures have made viable, and the difficult sites we are now often asked to use are only possible because of sophisticated methods of designing and constructing foundations.

Similarly, conditions in the industry are subject to constant change. New materials and plant are introduced, new calculation methods allow construction to closer tolerances, and as labour becomes inexorably more expensive, mechanical methods of construction, including factory-line production, are seen as consequently relatively economical. Factory production, the use of plant, the need to maintain desirable modern safety standards each impose their own restraints which affect the equation.

Where appearance is concerned we should, of course (and as I have previously indicated) beware of any deliberate attempt to appear stylishly modern. The principles of aesthetics are timeless – and an honest response to the conditions mentioned above will give a fresh enough look to our work. There is a danger in attempting to obtain an up-to-date look by the use of fashionable devices – the process may catch the eye and deter close examination of the essentials of a design for a time, but when these gimmicks inevitably date, the basic weakness of the work may be revealed all too clearly.

Many people may choose to live in houses fifty, a hundred or several hundred years old. They do so, in general, because they hate the conformity they believe will be imposed by habitation of one of a row of similar newer houses, because of the situation of the house or because its irregularities due to alterations and settlement over years give it charm. They know well that in practical terms they must sacrifice many modern standards. Such a house will have been designed to accommodate the life-style of a past age, using obsolete methods, and will need considerable adaptation if it is to suit informal modern life, provide a light and warm environment, and be economical to heat and maintain. People like the irregular and weathered appearance, however: perhaps the competition between householders on modern estates leads to brashness of appearance which ought to be modified.

Fig. 2.5 The design of the modern house also responds to demands created by the way in which it will be used and the way it will be built, as well as the way we want it to look

A modern house like the one shown in Fig. 2.5 will be designed to accommodate a modern life-style with emphasis on leisure activities, kitchen meals as a possibility if not the norm, study bedrooms for teenagers, whole house heating and room for the car, and will offer privacy even on a high-density development. The standards of amenity reached are beyond the dreams of any but the richest householders of the previous generation.

It seems probable that it will always be the case that needs and demands – and the means to satisfy them – will be subject to rapid change. In thirty years time we may, due to a communications revolution, return to a mediaeval pattern of home-centred work. We could each (consider the Open University, Bureaufax, Telex) work within the confines of our own home, keeping in touch with colleagues through audio-visual links. We should need larger houses, but office blocks would be obsolete – and would we need cars?

Alternatively, with increasing power costs the private car might disappear; making the siting of homes close to public transport links vital. It is amusing to speculate on possible trends, but essentially useless. We must design for present conditions while recognising the constant evolutionary trends that persist.

This makes it essential to take a systematic, and as objective as possible, approach to design. Problems should be tackled as though they were arising for the first time because this is, essentially, the case. One facet or another will be new, or have new importance, even if this is the fifth factory building on the same industrial estate that we have tackled. The new factor is always liable to upset the balance of the entire problem, so tinkering won't do – we must go back to first principles.

It is always tempting to take a satisfactory solution from the past and amend it a little to meet a new condition. For example, a hotel chain might want a new seaside hotel to be similar to one that was operating satisfactorily in a tourist area of great scenic beauty. They might recognise the higher proportion of children likely among the guests at the seaside, and propose to meet this by simply adding a proportion of 'family' rooms to the accommodation. This could appear to be a simple matter, but would miss the point that the children would demand playrooms, meals at unconventional times, and extra laundry facilities – and would trail sand through the corridors to boot. Perhaps this example is too obvious, but it makes the point. All alterations to the programme have consequences, they do not stand alone.

The new problem is different from the previous one, and needs to be thought through.

Creative problem-solving

One widely adopted and very satisfactory method used for design is that known as 'creative problem-solving'.

This is an 'objective' (as opposed to a subjective) method that attempts to exclude preconceived ideas, prejudices, and the following of well-worn habits of thought. It is a system applicable to the solution of a wide variety of everyday problems, and especially those in building.

The process is broken-down into a series of sequential stages, and it is an important principle that they should be thoroughly tackled in turn, the temptation to leapfrog being resisted determinedly.

Analysis and assimilation

It is always useless – and frequently prevents a final satisfactory outcome – to attempt to solve a problem which has not first been thoroughly analysed. Problems are not always what they seem. There was the kitchens supervisor who would on no account have cupboards under sinks – not on any hygenic grounds, but because (it emerged eventually) she had been used to using a sink with a cupboard below,

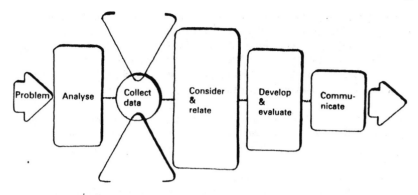

Fig. 2.6 Good design results from the application of systematic methods

whose handle laddered her tights and bruised her shins. When it was pointed out that a cupboard door could have recessed handles, she was happy to agree to the cupboards. She had misunderstood the problem

It is common for people to begin crystallising their intentions on the basis of the final result they think they WANT, rather than trying to work out rationally what their NEEDS are. This is liable to lead to the repetition of conventional answers, and limits originality and progress.

For example, many families wishing to build their own home will express their desires in terms of the number and size of the rooms they want. Challenged, they will be able to explain that families 'like theirs' live in houses of about that size, and that they feel they should, too. It is only when they have it clearly explained that a truly tailor-made house (which is presumably what they want if they have asked for an individual design rather than buying from a developer) will take account of the individual personalities and needs of THEIR particular family, which may need quite a different kind of accommodation, that they see the need to describe their life-style as the architect asks.

Similarly, school governors may state how many classrooms and specialised teaching spaces their new school must have. This will be based on experience in their old, obsolete and thoroughly unsatisfactory building – but they may fail to appreciate that less than satisfactory teaching patterns have been forced upon their staff, and are in danger of being perpetuated.

It is not enough, either, simply to define the accommodation required in terms of space (or even, in a more sophisticated way, in terms of operations to be accommodated). The site, with all its idiosyncrasies of shape and levels, planting and services, surroundings and easements may have a profound effect on the design. So may cost limits, so may time constraints, so may the selection of a particular method of construction, material or service system.

If design begins before the problem has been stated in detail and the whole of the relevant information obtained and understood, decisions may be taken which are ill-judged, but which are exceedingly difficult to alter because they become part of the basis of all that follows. The very earliest decisions must be right, and they must not therefore be approached before the problem to be solved has been defined.

Such definition will naturally include an appreciation of priorities. It is rare indeed for a solution to a problem as complex as those found in the building field to be perfect in every respect. Inevitably, compromises have to be made, and it is vital to know where this can be done, with the least damage.

This stage of design can be very lengthy – periods of one or two years are often quoted – but should not be skimped. It can be difficult to explain this to an impatient client.

Chapter 3 deals in detail with the collection of data in problems of building design.

Consideration

Having collected this mass of data, it is necessary to consider the relationships between and within the various groups of material. The factors will be different in every case, of course, but to take a simple example, there is clearly a relationship between cost, area and standards. If £100 000 is available, one can enclose 500 m^2 at £200/m^2 or 400 m^2 at £250 or 200 m^2 at £500. The quantity surveyor can provide data to show the implications of these choices, as well as the effect of building a compact shape rather than a sprawling one, the effect of using one part of the site in preference to another, and so on. The quantity surveyor is not making a decision – the designer will make a recommendation in the light of the expressed priorities of the client.

He may have to recommend that the wishes of the client cannot be met within the money made available, and ask for further instructions.

A more subtle relationship might emerge between, perhaps, the wish to produce a building with a 'traditional' flavour (a ski-lodge?) and the requirement for modern standards of amenity, or between the wish for a very compact design and demands for privacy between areas of accommodation. In either of these cases, fresh needs will be perceived when the relationships are examined, so that it is important that this should be conscientiously done.

At this stage there may be a temptation to attempt to produce a safe, workable solution to the problem as it emerges. This should be resisted, as the result is liable to be pedestrian, and less advantageous to the client than might otherwise be the case. Techniques such as 'brainstorming', or the use of lateral thinking have to be adopted deliberately to avoid this trap: we can all see the obvious answer, and may find ourselves committed to it to the extent of being unable to conceive of an alternative.

Brainstorming

In this case, having read and re-read, and thoroughly considered the data, the members of the design team sit down to think of every probable, possible, improbable and frankly impractical answer to the problem. They may be thinking about a major system, such as the circulation of patients in a hospital, or about a detail such as the selection of a floor finish. Since a simple example will demonstrate the method, let us consider the latter.

Everyone calls out, or writes down, every material he has ever heard of that might be even remotely usable. Nothing is discarded because it seems too ridiculous. The list might include conventional things like wood block or vinyl tiles, less obvious ones like cobbles or brick as well as unlikely ones like grass and persian carpet. The list is likely to run to scores, if not hundreds.

Subsequently, evaluation of the suggestions against the established criteria for the component will reduce the list to probables and eventually to the optimum selection.

The criteria for the floor finish in question will have been defined not only quantitatively but also in order of importance. The most *critical* will be used as first eliminator – perhaps, in our case, this might be that the appearance should remain good with daily washing at most, even when mud was coming in on shoes from outside. Persian carpet would clearly disappear, but our other suggestions would remain.

If the second priority was long life, with an optimum twenty-year renewal cycle, we should next eliminate grass – and so on. So the process would continue, through non-slip properties, reflectance, cost and acid resistance (or whatever considerations had been established) until only one or two materials remained. These would then have to be examined rigorously to ensure their viability, and a recommendation could be made. There seems no immediate reason why brick should not be acceptable, since weight is apparently not a criterion.

Brainstorming of this kind has been known to throw-up the idea of glass kitchen worktops, rosebushes instead of paving for 'no-go' areas, and firemens' poles for getting doctors to intensive care units quickly. It has also been successfully used as an approach to complicated engineering and economic problems.

Lateral thinking

It is also important, if creative work is to be performed, to cultivate the art of 'lateral thinking'. That is to say, the ability to escape from the tramlines of habitual thought forms, and to see problems from a new point of view.

An example came from a group of students challenged to provide covered playspace for a nursery school on a very tight budget. Some groups proposed begging scrap material, mobilising parent labour, or doing the job themselves in their spare time – the lateral notion came when it was suggested the money should be used to provide cagoules and wellingtons for the children so that the cover was unnecessary.

The suggestion that deserts could be irrigated by towing icebergs to them from the arctic on a regular basis (behind returning tankers?) the idea of running two shifts at a college instead of building an extension, and the notion of moving the homes to the centre of towns and the offices to the perimeter (so eliminating private motoring and letting travelling be done on expenses) are other lateral proposals.

From this 'consideration' stage, it will be seen that tentative solutions to the problem begin to emerge. It is important not to allow one possibility to become predominant, but to treat each as of comparable merit until rigorous evaluation has been completed.

Development

During the development of two or more of the tentative solutions which have now emerged, it is vital to keep two considerations firmly in mind:

1. At every point, decisions must be checked against the established criteria of the 'assimilation' stage.

    The criteria, and the priorities which have been laid down by an intensive process of analysis are not to be lightly set aside. As we all know, it is quite common for the client (or even a designer) at this stage to see some device or material that seems superficially attractive, and to be anxious to incorporate it in the scheme. Alas, this is sometimes done without reference back to the brief, and this can have the effect of making an important requirement unobtainable. For example, low maintenance may be a high-priority requirement – but a sudden infatuation with oiled teak might make someone overlook the care this material would require. The later disappointment that maintenance was not as minimal as hoped would be difficult to overcome.

    Even more, the material or service lightly selected could be fine in itself, but have unforeseen effects elsewhere in the design. Underfloor heating can dictate floor finishes, and the use of solid fuel will have an important effect on the possible sites for a plantroom.

    If at any point, the client appears to be changing the conditions of the brief (or overlooking them) the design team have a duty to draw his attention to this fact, point out the consequences that might ensue, and ask for firm instructions. The consequences may be so far-reaching that much completed design work has to be regarded as abortive.

It should not need to be said that the design team themselves should never be guilty of modifying or ignoring the brief in any way. If a requirement appears to be unattainable, this should be pointed out to the client: he will give instructions for any change. He alone is entitled to do so.

2. The widest and most influential decisions should be taken first, leaving questions of detail, and ones which do not have consequences where other matters are concerned, to be dealt with later.

This means that the position of the building on the site, the major massing, the floor levels or the structural grid may be very early decisions – or in a different case, the relationship to be obtained between an auditorium, back-stage areas and public circulation might be regarded as crucial.

It is most likely that an appreciation of the order in which decisions are to be arrived at will have to be made, and often it is useful to prepare a bar-chart programme or critical-path diagram to indicate vital cut-off dates. Everyone, including the client, needs to be aware of the programme, especially of the latest dates at which decisions can be reached, or after which alterations should not be made, without a consequent delay.

Once any decision is reached, it is of great importance that it should be regarded as final, and that every member of the design team can rely upon this. Should there be later changes, all subsequent and consequential decisions need re-examination. The new conditions established by the change may well have a profound effect on the overall balance of the brief, and require a different response. It is one of the most important principles of systematic design that decisions logically taken should not be reversed.

The development stage thus requires very considerable self-discipline on the part of everyone taking part in the process. From a very large range of possible options at the outset, the number is systematically reduced by the application of logical thought to problems in a descending order of importance. It rapidly becomes clear which of these options are viable, and every decision reduces the number of options subsequently available. Once an option, however apparently attractive, has been excluded, it should cease to enter the calculation of the team.

Chapter 8 deals with the 'consideration' and 'development' stages of design, as they apply to a particular building example.

Communication

It is a common fallacy to suppose that design and drawing are synonymous. This is not, of course, true. Design is a process applying logical thought to a problem – the design emerges in the designer's brain, and if, for example, he is a working potter, there will be no need for him to make a drawing at all . . . he will just get on with making the pot.

It is when design and production are divorced that the making of drawings becomes important, as well, of course, as when a client has to undertake to buy the product before it is made. A manufacturer could go ahead to produce a range of cars, basing his belief that they would sell on market research and his own experience. If the public doesn't like the cars, they don't buy.

In the case of building, the future owner is generally committed to buy before the foundations are dug, and so he, as well as the builder, needs to see drawings. The drawings the builder requires can and should be diagrammatic in character, and give clear instructions rather than an impression of what the finished job will look like. The client wants precisely such an impression. He needs to know realistically what he will be getting for his money.

The drawings which will convey the ideas of the designer to the client are therefore of the greatest importance. They should convey the solution proposed as realistically and understandably as possible as well as explaining why the particular proposals are being made rather than some alternative. It is unlikely that drawings from which the building could actually be constructed will be suitable for this purpose – perspective sketches, models and coloured elevations will be more informative to the client than the diagrams the builder needs.

Designers should guard against being carried away in the enthusiastic selling of their ideas. There is no place for false perspectives, impossible viewpoints or idealised colour. The surroundings should be faithfully depicted. The wish is to present the proposals truthfully, not to get them accepted at all costs!

Preparation of the drawings may be the shortest and least onerous stage of design, but it is of critical importance, since it is vital that the designer's response to the problem posed by the client should be accurately understood. It may well be a responsibility that is delegated to a technician.

Chapter 9 deals in detail with communication, and especially has regard to the types of drawings which can appropriately be employed in different circumstances.

Examples of problem solving

The whole process of creative problem-solving, including analysis and assimilation, consideration, development and communication stages is, as was mentioned earlier, applicable to a wide variety of simple and complicated problems.

Whether one is settling on a summer holiday, choosing a meal or putting a satellite into space, a systematic approach is necessary.

People take summer holidays for a wide variety of reasons, so that a fortnight by the sea in Spain is not the perfect answer to everyone's needs. Before progress can be made in the selection, one needs to know the benefits sought from the break: a complete change of pace, or of place; to see new ways of life; to visit beauty spots; a chance to learn or practice a sporting or artistic skill – or just to get the best tan in the office? Then, an idea of the money available is clearly important, as well as one of the total time to be filled, and the times of year that can be chosen. And, of course, in addition one needs a range of brochures, so as to see what is on the market in the way of packages, as well as an idea of geography and fares in case one decides to be independent. Having collected all this information, it is possible to start relating one's dreams to actual possibilities – and lateral thinking may indicate that helping with the grape harvest may be a cheap and relaxing change from the office, and a good way of getting a tan. At the development stage, one contacts actual potential employers, hostelries and transport companies, and perhaps enquires about the practicability of hitch-hiking. Communication becomes the actual putting into effect of the plans once made.

A sensible choice could not have been made, had not the reasons for taking a holiday and the resources available been first evaluated and then related to one another, so that impossibilities could be discarded. It was also vital to have kept a sufficiently open mind to see that lazing on a beach is not the only way of acquiring a tan, and that one can pay in other ways than hard cash.

Where choosing a meal is concerned, we may imagine this is a meal to be prepared at home, for guests one wishes to impress without overtly appearing to do so.

It will be important to prepare a well-balanced meal in dietary terms, a meal with contrasts of flavour and texture in it, one that is within one's capabilities as a cook – and one that will require a minimum of last-minute attention. The fact that one guest is a vegetarian and another on a strict gluten-free diet will restrict the choices, as will the extent of the housekeeping purse, however augmented. It will be important, too, to know what foods are readily available at the season, and at what cost.

If ease of preparation on the day is considered first priority, the earliest decision might be to have cold first and third courses, followed by fruit, cheese and coffee, and a slow-cooked casserole as a main dish. Details of major foods would next be settled – taking into account that each guest would need to reject some foods, and that this number should be limited for each of them. Then the details of auxiliary foods and garnishes would be settled. Finally a plan for preparation would be prepared. Triumphant service of the meal would form the 'communication' phase.

At the other end of the scale, a space programme could not exist if it were not based on closely stated and understood objectives, and most systematically developed with constant feedback and evaluation, and a precisely similar pattern of problem-solving is needed – but on a far more complex scale.

This will include many minor programmes for the solution of the ancillary problems that are vital to the success of the whole – the packaging of food for weightless conditions; the selection of a cladding material to protect the exterior against the heat of re-entry, the training of mechanics, the presentation of the programme to the public so as to obtain the necessary funding, and so on. Each of these will pass through the same stages outlined above, and additionally each will have its place in the grand master plan, within whose framework every aspect of the programme has to be considered in its due place. If this master did not control progress, the whole unwieldy structure would revolve interminably without ever reaching conclusions.

This provides an analogy for building. An overall programme, with target dates for the resolution of every important question, is essential to so complex an operation as the design of a building if any actual progress is to be made. Otherwise the team will always be bound (fallaciously) to feel that just a few more days thought will throw up a better answer to whatever the current problem may be. Each aspect of the job will, in its turn, be tackled in a similar manner, but the more complex the building the more essential the overall programme, applied with reasonable rigidity, will be.

Where a design team has to work together, under the coordination of an individual (generally, as we have seen, the architect) it is also important that each should understand clearly the boundaries of the area in which he is expected to reach conclusions, the aspects on which he will need to consult with colleagues, and the areas in which he must be prepared to defer to the greater expertise of others (or be overruled because some aspect of the work other than that within which he is concerned is considered of greater importance).

It is vital that the team leader should both carry overall responsibility for the work of the team and be the ultimate arbiter where conflicts of advice occur. Such conflicts are less likely if a well-knit and mutually trustful team work within a clearly understood framework of responsibilities than if a looser cooperation means that the boundaries of each person's sphere can easily be misunderstood.

As in so many aspects of life, accepted discipline enhances the actual freedom experienced.

In order that the application of the principles described to building design should be understood clearly, an imaginary project – for the design of a small factory building for a manufacturer of wooden toys – is developed in later chapters. Like all the examples chosen to illustrate various points and techniques throughout the book, this is a deliberately simple one. The application of the principles to a larger and more complex building would be more elaborate and time-consuming, but in essence the same.

Chapter 3

Defining the problem

The need for definition

It should be obvious that a problem cannot be solved until it has been defined, but unfortunately this doesn't seem to be the case. It is quite common for a client to believe that his needs will be met by a building exactly like one he has seen – or that, with slight modifications, an existing design might very well suit his case. It has to be admitted, too, that many occupants 'manage' in buildings that are far from tailor-made for their needs, and that there is sometimes a case for providing simple covered space that can be adapted to be used for many different purposes. Making do may be an acceptable short-term expedient, and it might work well for a client who had difficulty in predicting just how his needs were likely to develop over the years. He would, however, always have to compromise where convenience, or cost, or some other vital factor was concerned, and he should be made clearly aware of the inevitability of such sacrifices when settling on that option.

Every architectural design problem is, in fact, unique, and will have a unique solution. This solution will take proper account of all the needs of the client (which may include a degree of flexibility in use, and must certainly include his perception of priorities), of the limitations imposed by the budget, by the site, by the use of whatever materials and methods are chosen as appropriate, and by the wish to provide a building which is pleasant to work in and enhances the visual environment. The end result will be a building in which every requirement has been given due weight, and which is efficient to use, pleasant to live with and soundly built.

Difficulties in achieving this are bound to arise if information is not sought at an early enough stage, or if new requirements come to light after the design has begun to crystallise. Changes in the conditions, too, give rise to problems of coherent design.

A design prepared for one site, for example, can rarely, if ever, be transposed happily to another one. The levels will be different, access may be from a different side, the positions of and depths of the sewers are unlikely to match – there may be trees to be preserved. At best, such a transposition can only be a compromise. The features of the site need to be known when the earliest design decisions are taken, so that account can be taken of them from the start.

Similarly, an apparently slight change in the schedule of accommodation can affect a design to a seemingly disproportionate extent. Changing a bedroom into a living-room, for example, even if the size is constant, is more than a matter of altering the name on the plans. The relationships of the space to others in the design, the nature of the windows, the needs where power and other services are required, will all be different. If a washbasin is needed, the economy of the services for the whole house has to be reconsidered: different furniture to be accommodated may demand a different arrangement of windows and doors.

Another problem sometimes arises where insufficient consideration of costs at the outset leads to unrealistic expectations of the amount of space that can be bought with the available money. When tenders come in, costs have to be cut – and this can only be done at the expense of the overall design, whether standards of services or finishes are to be reduced, or a part of the building omitted. Earlier thought might have led to the choice of a more economical plan form or the use of a simpler structure. A change in these respects is impractical at so late a stage.

It also sometimes occurs that a design is invalidated because of failure to appreciate that the planning authority would stipulate the use of particular materials or roof form.

Though time and fees will be involved, it will always result in a more satisfactory end product in these cases if a new design is prepared rather than an old one adapted. It is only where the whole of the relevant information is available before any attempt to design is made that results that could be called architecture can be produced, and every effort should always be made to avoid abortive work by ensuring that data is collected, marshalled and understood as a prerequisite of the design process.

At this point it is appropriate to consider the notion of multi-use spaces. We see all around us buildings used for purposes other than those for which they were built.

Redundant churches have become homes or community centres or warehouses, redundant cinemas have become bowling rinks (and had, in turn, to be converted to yet other new purposes) and redundant warehouses have been adapted to provide offices or workshops or dwellings. There is a move, too, towards providing covered space without a predetermined use.

This does not mean, though, that there is no functional brief for such a building. There are still needs in terms of levels of light, temperature, ventilation and sound insulation: there are still access and escape to be considered: human scale is still likely to be an important consideration. The requirements of construction and appearance will carry their usual weight – and functionally the brief may have increased stringency because of the need to satisfy a spectrum of possible requirements (if the options of flexibility are to be preserved) rather than a limited range of closely defined ones.

Obtaining the whole of the information required at a sufficiently early stage can present problems, whatever the building type. For the majority of laymen – and for many semi-professionals who regularly commission buildings – it is far easier to react to and comment upon a developed design (whether that is a completed building or a set of drawings) than to define precisely what is required in advance. Most people can explain the feature they do not want much more easily than they can say what they do need. They tend, too, to confuse wants and needs, and to react positively to a familiar idea but reject a new one unless it is especially carefully presented.

They may also be hard to convince of the value of spending money at a stage many of them may regard as exploratory.

For these reasons it is very important to make clear to the client the great value of careful development of the brief before design work itself starts (beyond, of course, the initial stage of the feasibility study).

He needs to realise that this is a rigorous and time-consuming process which is necessary if he is to obtain the advantages of a purpose-built building for which he intends to pay.

The members of the design team, too, have to appreciate the extent to which quite small changes in requirements can invalidate earlier decisions, and to resist the prevalent temptation to begin to evolve design solutions before the whole of the data on which their decisions should be based is available. This demands considerable self-discipline.

The architectural technician is likely to have an important role in obtaining and presenting this body of material. He needs to be conversant with the sources from which it is available, the means by which it can be obtained, and appropriate methods of presentation in each case.

Relevance

There are, naturally, sensible limits to be defined in each particular case regarding the material which is relevant and necessary. In general it can be said that the commoner the building type, the less the special data that will be required. The amount of published data and experience readily at hand with regard to housing, for example, makes special market surveys necessary only in exceptional circumstances, while the design of a specialised laboratory to accommodate some novel line of research would involve extensive investigations. Thought by the architect, in consultation with the design team, is needed to determine the limits of relevance in each particular case.

Priorities

An even more critical task, to be undertaken in close consultation with the client, has regard to the relative weight to be given to each set of requirements. Which of these are to be regarded as paramount and immutable, and where may judicious compromises be made? For example, the only site available for an old persons' home might have difficult levels. Is economy to be all important (in which case a sprawling building following the contours might be chosen) or will easy access to all parts of the building by residents be so vital as to justify the extra expense of more complicated foundations for a compact block?

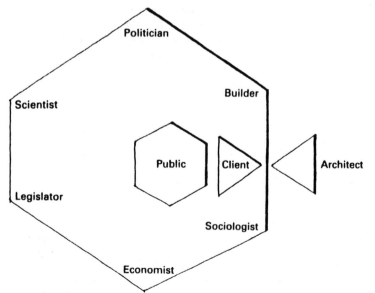

Fig. 3.1 The influences on the eventual design solution are varied

The conflict has to be recognised and explained to the client, ensuring that he has a grasp of the implications of alternative strategies. It is he who knows, in terms of the whole life of the building, where the right decision lies. He must be guided towards an informed decision, which will form part of the 'brief' for the design.

At every stage of design, members of the design team find themselves making choices between alternative solutions to detailed problems, as well as the major ones. It is only where the priorities among the many and often clashing requirements of the brief have been established in advance that sensible decisions can be reached.

The information needed

The kinds of information needed before design work should start fall roughly into three categories:

1. There is the data that is part of the background of education and experience of the designer, and is likely to be relevant whatever the particular problem being faced: technology, anthropometrics, terotechnology, law.
2. There is a wealth of available expertise in particular building types or recurrent problems (hospitals or foundations for mining areas, for example) which the firm may have readily available because of their previous experience, but will in any case know where to find in published form, in design guides and bulletins, practice notes and Building Research Establishment digests, for example.
3. There is the data about the site, the special requirements of the client and so on, which are peculiar to the particular commission, and which must be collected afresh in every case.

Sources of information

Experience

Very commonly, a client will choose a designer because he knows that the firm in question has experience in the kind of building he's interested in.

In this way, firms can build-up a very useful body of expertise over the years. The danger that goes along with this advantage is that they may become repetitive in the solutions they offer and may not scrutinise each new commission with the detachment another firm might bring to bear. There may also be a tendency to wish to develop a line of evolution within the building type, and as a result to give less than due weight to the idiosyncrasies of individual cases.

Design teams (in public as well as private offices) who have become experts in hospitals or housing or leisure centres can find it useful and refreshing to face the challenge of a totally different kind of problem. The client who approaches a designer who does NOT display an already developed experience of the particular building type should not be worse served than the one who goes to a specialist.

The specialist may, of course, feel that he runs a more efficient office because he does not have to go back to first principles on every job. It is to be hoped that he is prepared to go back to first principles sometimes, and will so avoid producing stereotyped work.

Of the three types of material described above, the first needs keeping up-to-date through alert attention to developments in the industry – perhaps by attending meetings of professional bodies, retraining courses, and manufacturers' displays as well as by thoughtful attention to the technical press. The second can be kept up-to-date by working in a specialist environment, provided the narrow view that this provides does not blinker the team to outside developments. The third needs to be obtained afresh in every case, no matter what the expertise of the team involved.

Examples

All designers will want to see examples of similar building types to the one facing them. If visits can be arranged, so much the better. This gives an opportunity to talk, not to the people who commissioned and designed the building, but to those who occupy and maintain it, whose point of view may be rather different.

This is an opportunity to discover what the good and bad points of the building have turned out to be in practice. It isn't a chance to steal someone else's ideas! The visit ought to be paid in company with the client, because it is most importantly HIS chance to crystallise his ideas as to his precise requirements. He may have to be counselled to avoid describing those needs in terms of amendments to the design he has just visited, however.

Existing examples, of course, should always be looked at a trifle sceptically. It is a long time since they were built, and conditions – and ideas – may have changed. Be clear, too, that the problem was NOT the same one now being considered. It can be useful to consider in what ways their problem influenced the detailed design these people came up with. At least that may avoid features irrelevant to the new problem from being transferred to it.

Published material

There is a natural tendency, when faced with an unfamiliar design problem, for the designer to turn to the technical press to discover how others have tackled similar tasks. Without any imputation of a wish to plagiarise, it is necessary to suggest care in this exercise. The solution on which someone else has settled, especially when beautifully presented in prose, drawings and photographs, exercises a subtle

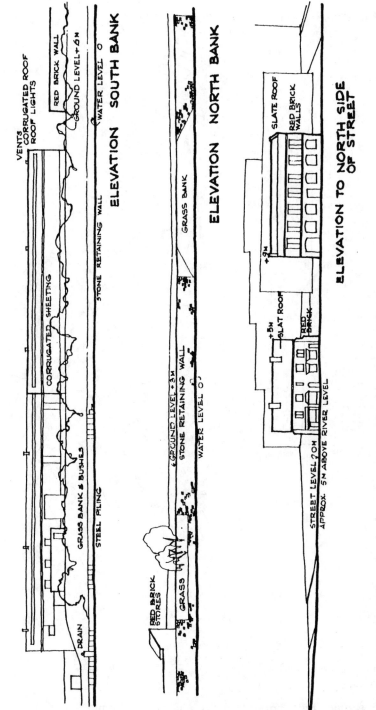

Fig. 3.2 The design team needs a record of the surroundings of the site

44

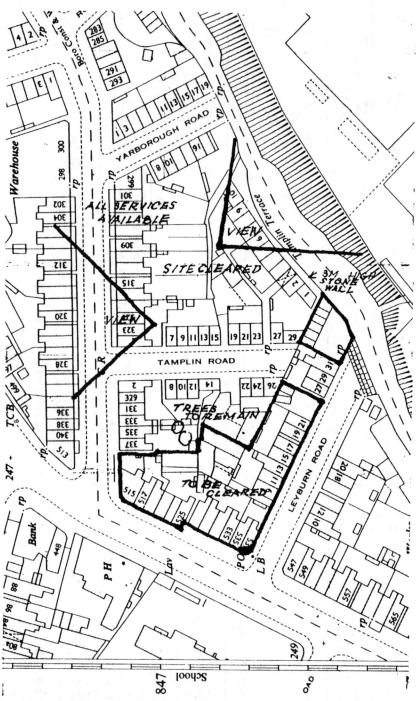

Fig. 3.3 A quick record of observations on site can be plotted on the Ordinance Survey map

fascination that can inhibit the development of ideas particularly appropriate to the conditions of the present case.

Everyone wishes to know the 'state of the art', of course, before he starts work. He should bear in mind two points, however. The first is that the building illustrated is a response to a different problem from the one that confronts him now, and the other is that the design he is examining was, in all probability, produced some years earlier. It has, after all, gone through a lengthy process before emerging as a completed, occupied building, and catching the eye of the press.

Everyone in a design office has to keep up-to-date, in respect of design notions as much as technical ones, and the magazines need to be read and probably filed for reference. The articles one sometimes sees, describing buildings revisited after a period of years, should be filed alongside the original eulogies too: perhaps one of the most useful functions of press write-ups is to help us avoid the mistakes others have made before us.

The site

The influence of site conditions on the design is covered in Chapter 5. There is a wealth of information available regarding every piece of land in the country, notably through the Ordnance Survey, and the Land Registry may be able to provide useful data. This information may provide sufficient back-up to a personal inspection to allow a feasibility study to be made: it is dangerous to base a developed design upon it.

The principal sources of information regarding a site are set out below.

1. Personal inspection, which should be recorded in sketches and photographs, and notes superimposed on a large-scale Ordnance Survey map. This will provide a basic understanding of the levels, dimensions and special features of the site and its surroundings, which may be sufficient for sketch design purposes. Attention should be paid not only to the character of the surrounding development, but also to its condition (Figs. 3.2, 3.3).

2. Survey A detailed record of the physical conditions on the site on the day the survey was made. This gives detailed information on lines of boundaries, levels, existing features (including planting) and is accurate enough to allow precise placing of the building. Levels are most usefully shown both as a close grid of spot levels and as interpolated contours (Fig. 3.4).

3. Site investigation At least a trial pit should be dug to ascertain the nature of the ground sufficiently to determine whether special attention to foundations or waterproofing will be necessary. If potential problems can be identified sufficiently early, they can often

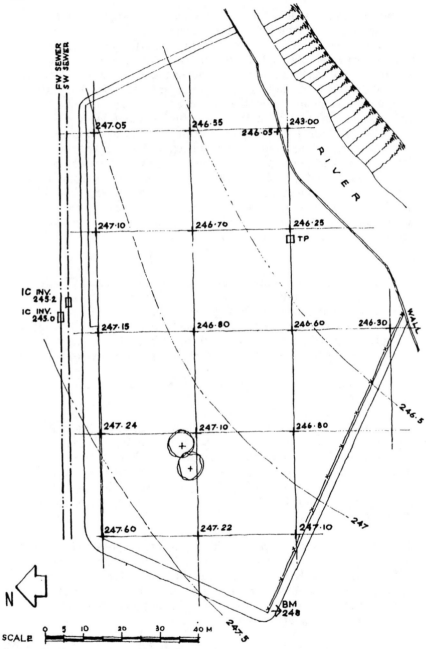

Fig. 3.4 An accurate survey is required before design work can develop far

BOREHOLE No

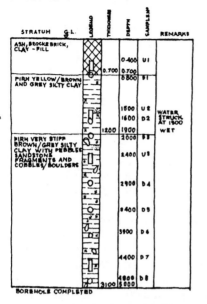

Fig. 3.5 The site investigation gives further vital information

be circumvented. If there has been recent excavation on adjoining sites, information based on conditions there may be adequate. The presence of underground watercourses, if suspected, should always be confirmed or excluded (Fig. 3.5).

4. Mining   If there have been, or may be in the future, mining operations beneath the site, the National Coal Board should be consulted to provide details of their workings and their recommendations of precautions that should be taken.

5. Ownership   The solicitor can provide information of head landlord's rights, or of easements that might affect the use of the land. Such requirements can usually be accommodated easily provided they are known at an early enough time, but can spell near disaster to a developed scheme if discovered too late. (See Ch. 13).

6. Public utilities   The undertakers should be invited to provide details of the positions, capacities and depths of their services in the vicinity, which can have a critical effect on design.

Town hall

It is always desirable to discuss proposals for development with the planning and enforcement officers who will be concerned as early as possible during the project. In this way, their requirements will be discovered – but also the way may be prepared if, later, there is the wish to reach agreement on any proposals that might strike these officials as controversial or unconventional. They are not unnaturally more prone to be sympathetic to someone who has canvassed their opinion than to someone who has seemingly put in a rather odd proposal without any consultation!

Public

In the case of any prominent building the public has a right to be consulted about what is being done to its surroundings. Publication of plans or a model can, of course, lead to controversy and delay, and is sometimes avoided on that account. It is best to invite public comment through a carefully worded questionnaire or reaction forms, and to give a deadline for the receipt of comments.

Public opinion should really, of course, be expressed through the democratic process, and we should be able to suppose that the requirements of the planning authority were an expresssion of it. This is not, however, always a sufficient consultation of affected neighbours.

Even in the case of a minor building, it may be politic to seek a meeting with adjoining owners to explain the proposals and ensure that they do not feel aggrieved by them.

Consulting the public is difficult before there are concrete ideas to discuss. It may have to be on the basis of the feasibility study or of alternative tentative proposals.

Technology

Even at so early a point, some consideration of methods of construction that seem appropriate may be needed. It may be that the demands of a remote site or of unskilled labour force the adoption of low technology, or that the planning authority insists on the choice of particular materials or roof profile in a conservation area. In such cases, some additional research (additional, that is to the vocabulary of construction techniques with which all competent designers are equipped) may be required into the constraints in terms of spans, perhaps, or window sizes or wall thicknesses that particular choices may enforce (Fig. 3.6).

Costs

The client will inevitably have set cost limits, and it is a duty to stay within them wherever this is practicable – and where it is not, to point out the effects of the limits and any relaxation that is needed. For this to be feasible, the indispensable tool is the cost plan, which can and should be prepared by the quantity surveyor on the basis of published cost analyses. This design aid is discussed in detail in Chapter 12. It allows constant monitoring of the cost effect of design decisions, and

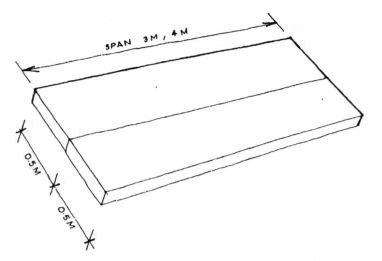

Fig. 3.6 It is important that a constructional method should not be adopted without full understanding of the constraints it will impose on design

permits the client to be kept in constant touch with the extent to which his expectations are realistic.

Client

The most important source of information, it goes without saying, is the client. He may be supposed to know what he needs, but it commonly takes considerable helpful direction before he can express his requirements in a useful form. He has to be guided in analysing his underlying needs, and helped to separate them from the half-formulated ideas of completed solutions he has in his head – and to see those needs as objectively and rationally as possible.

It is also important to be sure that not only the needs of the owner, who is paying for the building, but also the needs of those who will use and maintain the building on a day-to-day basis, are examined. This may entail extensive consultations, and the setting-up of internal committees and subcommittees – and can lead to interdepartmental squabbles from which the design team should aim to remain detached. Designers and their staffs will need to be easily available, though, to ensure that the brief is expressed in a form that does not presuppose a particular design solution. Any tendency on the part of the client to talk in terms of a specific solution to the problem must be gently discouraged. It is his business to set the problem – he is paying the designers to solve it.

To take an example of the separation of problem and solution, consider the design of an individual house. The family might wish to avoid setting a space apart specially for meals, but see only the alternatives of a dining/kitchen or a living/dining-room, neither of which they felt was entirely satisfactory. Many families would feel they must opt for one decision or the other, in order to guide their architect. They would by doing so tie his hands, however. If instead, they said that a separate dining-space was unnecessary, but that a space other than kitchen or living-room was preferred to eat in, they might be offered the option of a dining/hall, or a study/dining-room, or some other alternative, for consideration. The client should not suppose that only the alternatives of which he is aware are available – otherwise, why should he pay a specialist to prepare a design?

First, the client has to be encouraged to explain in as simple terms as possible the process which his building is to house. This will seem obvious to him, and he may need encouragement to state what seems so obvious, to his experts. Even if the 'process' is family life, he must explain the lifestyle of the particular family involved, otherwise the designer will act on assumptions that seem to HIM obvious, but are irrelevant to the case. The client has to state whether everyone gets up at the same time, whether family meals are the rule, how much entertaining is done and how formal it is, and so on. No one else knows.

He should be discouraged from talking about rooms, and encouraged to think of activities: the rooms will be the solution to the problem the activities set.

Having discussed these activities, and their relationships to others, he can be asked about the space and equipment each requires, about associated services and storage requirements, and about critical levels of temperature, light, sound and ventilation. This allows a detailed picture of the total requirements to be built-up, without reference to a particular building design.

A useful technique by which all this information can be obtained is the briefing chart (Fig. 3.7). Here the activities are listed on the left, while three broad, subdivided, columns ask specific questions about the nature of the space required for each. From a briefing chart of this kind, generally completed by design team and client in consultation, a specification for the spaces actually required can be built up.

An important part of this specification will be a circulation diagram, like the one shown in Fig. 3.8, which gives (in graphical form) the necessary relationships between the various spaces, without reference to structural constraints. Notes regarding the more critical special features of each space can usefully be added to such a diagram.

The chart and diagram given, which refer to the elementary industrial building mentioned before, are of course very simple. For a more complex building there would most likely be master diagrams describing the requirements and relationships between departments, supported by detail diagrams of the internal organisation of each area.

These drawings, together with plans of the site showing its features, limitations and services, photographs of the surroundings,

Job No.	Briefing chart Arrangement				Shape			Features				Floor surface	Wall surface	Remarks
	Share with	Next to	Near to	Floor	Aspect	Size	Equipment	Light	Humidity	Temperature	Power			
ENTER		Control, Reception	Admin.	G.F.		3 sq.m	chairs							overflow
MATERIALS INWARD		Control, Security	Materials Store	G.F.		3 sq.m	desk, loading bay							
MATERIALS STORAGE		Woodworking				15 sq.m	shelves		*					
CONTROL	Reception, Security					2 sq.m	desk, telephone							
SECURITY	Control					2 sq.m	desk, telephone							
RECEPTION	Security					2 sq.m	desk, counter, telephone							
ADMINISTRATION	Meetings		Reception			7 sq.m	2 desks							
TYPING	Filing					5 sq.m	2 desks							
FILING	Typing					2 sq.m	4 cabinets							
MEETINGS	Admin.		Typing		SW-SE	5 sq.m	board table for 6							
WOODWORKING		Materials Storage		G.F.		30 sq.m	Se machine layout	*	*		3-phase	dustfree hard	washable	dust extraction
FINISHING		Woodworking				20 sq.m	Se machine layout	*	*		3-phase	dust free		fume extraction
GOODS STORE		Finishing, Despatch		G.F.		20 sq.m	shelving		*					security
GOODS DESPATCH	Goods in	Goods Store				35 sq.m	loading bay							
REST		Enter	Woodworking		SW-SE	6 sq.m	couch, chairs, cooker							

Fig. 3.7 The briefing chart is one technique by which the design team can be sure they have asked the client all the right questions

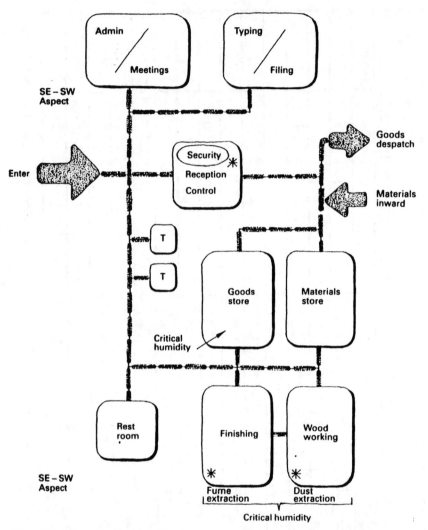

Fig. 3.8 The circulation diagram expresses much of the information from the briefing chart graphically

information regarding methods of construction considered appropriate, the cost plan, and (most importantly) the assessment of priorities, may be bound to form the brief. More information on appropriate methods of communication will be found in Chapter 9, and it should be remembered that the object is to present all the relevant facts in a form in which they may be easily assimilated by all members of the design team before design work begins. Presentation of the mass of data in an easily apprehended form is a vital prerequisite of successful design, and this is a task that may fall to the architectural technician.

It cannot be overemphasised that a design which is based on tinkering with previous solutions to slightly different problems, or which results from a cherished design idea clung to whatever else has to go by the board, or which is completed on the basis of guesses rather than facts, is bound to be less than perfect.

We all know that a good deal of work-a-day building is done on one or another of these bases – and clients seem reasonably happy with it. There is no doubt that they are happier with buildings where their designers have done their homework properly at the start; that these are the buildings owners are actively proud of and that are generally admired; and that our visual environment would be a good deal more enjoyable if such a rigorous approach was more common.

Chapter 4

Functional constraints

Motivations influencing building

The earliest buildings were, of course, dwellings, and it seems that man started (in the first place) simply to enhance the cave, or the hole in the ground, or other natural shelter, he had managed to find. We can probably ascribe four motives to him, and these are motives which still operate powerfully today – though our sense of the priorities may have changed.

Shelter

The difficulties, in almost all climates, of carrying on even the most basic activities of the preparation and consumption of food, let alone the more sophisticated ones of discussion and relaxation, in wide variations of weather conditions must have been an early and influential force in causing the initiation of building activity. If no cave provides natural shelter from rain, no tree provides shade, it is sensible to labour to provide such amenities artificially. Gradual and lengthy sophistication as man's capabilities have increased has led to more and more stringent demands being made, until some think we are in danger of forgetting that our clothing, too, can provide a measure of waterproofing and thermal insulation – to take the simplest examples.

Safety

We still expect, as no doubt the earliest builders did, that our security will be increased by the shelters we construct. We are less interested than he in predatory animals, and perhaps more so in those of our fellow men who might prey upon our property, but the principle that each man's house is his castle, and that he can relax in safety there, remains the same.

Privacy

Another powerful motivating force is the desire for screening from prying eyes for many of our activities. This may in one society appear as a desire for individual segregation, in another for segregation between age groups or sexes, and in yet another as a wish to protect the privacy of family activities. In each society some functions are considered particularly intimate, and a dropping of barriers in one area is generally compensated for by an accompanying rise in secrecy and concealment elsewhere.

Today, the unpopularity of 'picture' windows indicated by their heavy draping in nylon net, shows that this force still operates. Acute distress has been caused on some estates by the design of houses with such windows facing one another – a situation exacerbated by 'through' rooms where pairs of windows throw the occupants into relief, thus making it easy for passers-by to see them.

Status

It seems, also, that from primitive times people have wanted to express their personality and their place in society through their buildings. The tribal chief would occupy a dwelling larger and more richly decorated than the others – and all would aspire to similar

Fig. 4.1 The result of NOT 'keeping up with the Jones's?'

splendour. Such discontent would be highly advantageous as it would lead to a continuous improvement in standards, as the élite tried to keep ahead of an imitative herd. No doubt if such 'keeping up with the Jones's had not occurred we should all still be occupying the most primitive huts (Fig. 4.1).

Though all of the above refers to houses, it is of course relevant to every other kind of building as well. As houses came to be used as shops, workplaces, temples and so on, the need for their purpose to be apparent increased. Accommodation became specialised, shelter was still imperative, and security of temple treasure or privacy for trade secrets might increase in importance. The same essential needs evident for houses can be identified.

In every particular case it is, of course, important that as well as being aware of these four inherent demands the designer should understand the detailed demands being made upon the spaces being proposed. The priorities to be accorded will need to be evaluated separately for each case, but the order in which the major points are considered below will serve as a basis for any necessary reassessment.

Functions of the building envelope

Definition of space

It is often forgotten that the structures of a building are nothing but boundaries. What are important are the spaces that are enclosed.

Architecture has much more to do with the design of these spaces than with the design of walls, foundations and roofs, which is one of the fundamental ways in which it differs from building.

The first and predominant function of any building structure is that it cuts-up space into useful chunks of suitable shapes and sizes for the activities to be performed in them. It is the accommodation provided, in the last analysis, that matters – whether function, technical excellence or appearance is being considered.

The shape of each space has to be thought out so that it provides, three-dimensionally, just the accommodation needed. This is bound to demand analysis of the precise function to be carried on, the number of people who will be involved and the speed and energy requirements of the task. There is a good deal of published data around, but this does not obviate the need for individual study.

Anthropometrics

It was during the eighteenth century that explorers investigating the characteristics of newly discovered tribes found the need for objective data. By making comparative measurements it was found that racial features and similarities would reveal relationships between groups which might illuminate past population migrations and make valuable contributions to the developing science of anthropology.

Georges Cuvier developed this tool into a science in its own right, naming this 'anthropometrics', or the measurement of man. Today, this has medical applications – for example in monitoring the progress of certain glandular conditions, and in both establishing norms of physical development and comparing the growth of individuals with that norm. The regular measurement of schoolchildren for height and weight serves these twin purposes. The weighing of babies at infant welfare clinics exemplifies a further application of the principle, to assess nutritional status in individuals – a process developed further where there is a more severe risk of malnutrition or obesity.

It will be apparent that it is essential, if such comparisons are to have any validity, for a large mass of relevant, comparable and up-to-date information to exist. It is essential for the rate of growth of a twelve-year-old boy in Birmingham to be checked against a group of boys of the same age in the same place and at the same time.

Other information might be distorted by outside factors, such as general change in diet or atmospheric pollution.

The principle then, is that data from a large 'peer' group should be collected – a sample sufficiently numerous to have statistical credibility – as a context against which an individual case can be evaluated (Fig. 4.2).

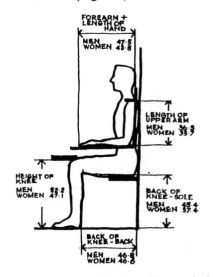

Fig. 4.2 Careful control is needed to ensure that anthropometric data collected is truly comparative

Once collected, it should be obvious that such data can be very valuable indeed for other purposes. For example, retailers of clothing can discover the proportions of persons of various sizes among the specific segment of the market to whom they hope to sell, and thus avoid turning away custom while their rails are full of garments in sizes

58

that no one wants. Hard-headed businessmen know that the range of sizes they need to stock in Manchester for sale to middle-aged managers will be different from that needed by a market consisting of teenagers in Brighton. They would say, no doubt, that they drew this information from experience and business acumen: they would none-the-less be applying anthropometric principles, especially when proposing to enter a hitherto untapped market.

This same data is clearly of great importance to designers of buildings. We may be forced to standardise: the single door size established must be convenient for use by a large majority of the population – the size chosen has to be based on established data on stature, and has varied over the centuries, and from place to place.

We are much aware of the importance of such considerations when we begin to design for children and we consult authorities on the correct lavatory basin height or arrangement for coat pegs for each age group when working on a school (Fig. 4.3).

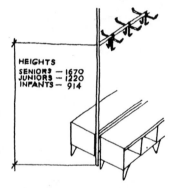

HEIGHTS
SENIORS — 1670
JUNIORS — 1220
INFANTS — 914

Fig. 4.3 Anthropometric data is greatly used in the design of schools

In the design of kitchens, too, and design for the elderly and disabled, there has been a good deal of emphasis on anthropometrics in recent years. This tends to spread beyond the simple measurement of stature and reach described above (which can be called 'static' anthropometrics) into two further areas.

The first of these is known as *dynamic* anthropometrics.

Dynamic anthropometrics takes into account not merely size but also the 'envelope of space' occupied by a person performing a particular task. Considerations of speed become significant. This can perhaps best be understood by considering the different amount of space required by an athlete when competing in a high-jump competition, in comparison with the very much smaller space he would occupy while sitting to watch his rival (Fig. 4.4).

Anyone who has queued for the cinema will have experienced the fact that a stationary line of people occupied less space than the same line in movement: when the doors open, the front of the queue begins to move long before the end.

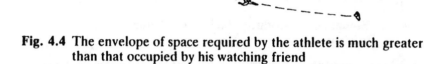

Fig. 4.4 The envelope of space required by the athlete is much greater than that occupied by his watching friend

The design of spaces for particular activities needs to pay special attention to this concept, if space is to be efficiently used. A proper appreciation of it might lead to a reduction in bills for heating underused spaces, and provision of adequate elbow-room where it is actually needed. The relevance to the design of escape routes will be evident.

The further development which takes into account not merely size and speed but energy expenditure as well is the concept well known in industry as *ergonomics*. To do a job with minimum effort is obviously efficient, and reduces danger because of the reduction in fatigue. To maximise the advantages, bending and stretching have to be eliminated from repetitive tasks, dials and controls need to be arranged so that the most important are placed where they can most readily be read or reached, and the total comfort of the operator has to be considered (Fig. 4.5).

Less application of these principles has, in the past, been made to building design than has been the case with dynamic anthropometrics. An exception is in the design of kitchens, especially for the disabled or elderly, where the recommended placing of storage has applied ergonomics. It is a science which should be in the thoughts of any designer if the environment he creates might lead to fatigue and danger if ill-considered.

Anthropometric data nowadays can be collected by rapid photographic techniques, screening large and closely defined peer groups, and need not depend on laborious measurement by tapes and callipers as in the past.

Care is needed to ensure that conditions are indeed standardised: for example, if the optimum table height for a group is being assessed,

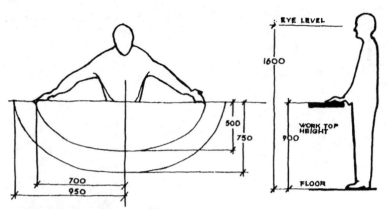

AVERAGE REACH OF PERSON SITTING AT DESK. TO REACH
OUTER AREA,THE USER WILL HAVE TO BEND BUT NOT
STAND UP

Fig. 4.5 Ergonomics introduces the idea that fatigue should be
minimised

should the people being measured each first be found their optimum
chair-seat height, or should the chair be standardised?

There are certain rules of thumb that can loosely be applied. For
example, a comfortable sitting position is generally related to
continuous support under the thighs while the lower leg is
perpendicular to the floor. It is usually thought that a standing
worker will be able to lay his palms flat on a worktop without leaning
forward, if the worktop is of convenient height, and the lowest
comfortable sink allows the knuckles to be rested on its base, again
without bending.

However, in such multi-purpose spaces as kitchens, particular
tasks vary in the frequency with which different actions are necessary.
Most equipment in buildings (in contrast to industry) has to serve a
multitude of purposes, and adaptability is important. Compromises are
inevitable, therefore, but they should be made in the light of careful
consideration of the purposes for which the facilities will be used for the
larger proportions of the time, as well as those actions where safety is
most critical.

Published anthropometric data is easily found, the Department of
the Environment bulletins *Space in the Home* and *Spaces in the Home*
being important sources that will be familiar. Such information,
however, though very valuable, needs to be treated with certain
reservations.

Firstly, it is inevitably out-of-date. As an example, consider the
size of housewives in the last generation. Not only has a generation of
mainly slight stature ceased to be active, but a new age group of young
giantesses has grown-up to take their place. Additionally, it has
become far commoner for husbands to carry their share of kitchen

chores. When was the data collected, and on what basis, on which the 'standard worktop height' and so on are based? Should it be reassessed?

Secondly, there is a danger in applying standard data to particular individual cases, and designers should have in mind that their client or the potential users of accommodation may not be typical of the population. Is data drawn from the whole population applicable for the narrower group of nurses, for example?

Thirdly, if accommodation is designed too precisely to conform to the needs of a particular function, there will be a loss of very necessary flexibility in use, and the imposition of rigid behaviour patterns may result. Buildings have a long life, and should have sufficient tolerances built-in to allow evolving use.

Circulation diagram

The relationships between functions are also critical, and it is generally essential to prepare a 'circulation diagram' which will set out graphically (without reference to the detailed design of the individual spaces.) what the relationships between them are to be. Figure 4.6 shows how this can be done. Such a diagram should be prepared as an optimum to be aimed at, leaving considerations of practicability on one side for the time being. The diagram will indicate which functions can be carried on in the same shared space, which require separate but contiguous spaces, and which can be accommodated far apart (see also Ch. 3).

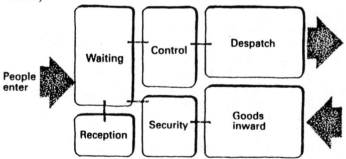

Fig. 4.6 Necessary relationships between the parts of accommodation have to be analysed if a sound solution is to be found

This purely functional information, however, must be used alongside an understanding of the aesthetic or sculptural effects that will be created. Sequences of lighter or darker, wider or narrower, small and large spaces must be consciously designed if the overall effect is to be successful. This not only gives interest to the design from the point of view of the occupant: the whole design is made more coherent and easily read because the effects created have been consciously arranged, and the building is easier and more enjoyable to use because of this.

This is an example of the difficulty of separating technical, functional and aesthetic considerations; the walls are being seen to perform the FUNCTION of defining a sculptural space, and the choice of materials, structural forms and so on contributes to this function.

The boundary structures of the spaces naturally have an effect on the way in which the spaces are appreciated. The choice of transparent window or solid wall, the use of roof-lighting, the presence of heavy beams or a soaring vault all affect the experienc? of being in the space. Spaces are made to seem closed or open, tortuous or simple, by the nature of the structures chosen to define them.

It must never be forgotten, though, that the structures exist to surround the spaces, not the spaces to allow the structures to be seen. Were this not the case, we would be putting up follies, not buildings.

Modulation of the environment

A second vital function of boundary structures is to modify the environmental characteristics of the spaces within them: the function, perhaps, that began as 'shelter'. Nobody, it seems, really knows objectively what 'comfort' conditions are – perceptions of comfort vary with individuals, and even then can be affected by health and mood. The best we can do is to try to obtain a balance of acceptable conditions. This is done under five important headings.

Water exclusion

The exclusion of unwanted water from the interiors of buildings remains one of their envelopes' most important functions. Few occupants will regard a building that leaks as satisfactory!

There are three sources of attacking water (apart from water which may inadvertently escape from service systems, which need not concern us). These are generally identified as precipitation, groundwater and condensation.

Precipitation Water from rain, hail, snow and mist will be blown about by the wind so that it attacks from all directions and does not merely descend vertically. Many of our traditional building details are a response to the absolute need to exclude precipitation from the interiors of buildings (Fig. 4.7). In our moderate climate we go to only moderate means in this respect, and it is worthwhile to examine the design strategies adopted where flooding is unavoidable or snow drifting is regularly anticipated (Fig. 4.8). As it becomes necessary in the UK to utilise more and more exposed sites – sites which might hitherto have been considered unacceptably vulnerable – it will be incumbent upon designers to re-examine their vocabulary of details to ensure that those adopted are adequate.

This applies, for example, to the height of flashings and

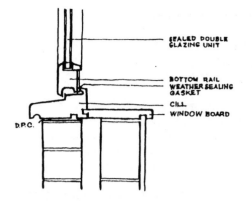

Fig. 4.7 The cill is designed to shed water, with a drip to prevent capillary movement

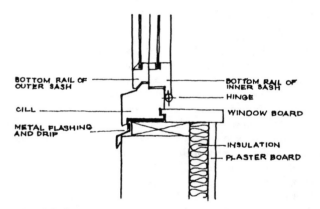

Fig. 4.8 In more extreme climates, more extreme precautions are needed

damp-proof courses, to the projection of roofs and to the protection of external doors. It is also frequently desirable to consider, on an exposed site, the positioning of doors to gain the most shelter.

It is not appropriate here to attempt to summarize a vocabulary of details. It should be pointed out, though, that the generally accepted ones must not necessarily be assumed to be suitable to every case. Designers need to have recourse to published weather data, particularly that relating to wind speed, rainfall levels and duration of storms when choosing appropriate defences for buildings.

Groundwater In a similar fashion, low-lying or particularly wet sites are regularly having to be used today because all the elevated and well-drained ones are already occupied. This exacerbates the problem of protecting the building from groundwater and makes care in choosing, detailing and placing damp-proof courses, damp-proof membranes and tanking vital.

In earlier days such precautions were less necessary because it was possible to select naturally protected sites. Later the basement (or in some cases the elevation of habitable rooms to first-floor level) provided suitable precautions.

These conditions no longer exist. A well-tried armoury of waterproofing methods has taken their place, but the designer should not assume that his habitual vocabulary will provide the answer to every problem. A combination of raised floor-levels, land drainage and tanking may be necessary in some cases but an extravagance in others – information on the level and pressure of the water table and the predicted incidence of flooding is required so that a suitable response to pre-existent conditions can be made.

It might be remembered that submariners don't depend on damp-proof courses – their craft are constructed of impermeable materials.

Condensation   In each of the cases referred to above, modern conditions force use of sites which would have been discarded by an earlier generation. In the case of condensation it seems that we have brought an escalation of trouble upon ourselves.

On the one hand, open fires with the forced ventilation that accompanies them, have become rare; and on the other, changes in the materials once used to materials of increased density lead to colder surfaces and therefore increased risk of condensation. Add to this that we are more conscious of the need to stop wastage of heat through open windows and by heating unoccupied rooms, and it becomes clear that humid conditions are likely to be normal.

To avoid the damp patches inevitable when such humidity condenses, and the damage to materials and finishes that would result, designers have found it essential to devise means (such as the psychometric chart) of predicting the dewpoints of the atmospheres they create (Fig. 4.9). They also need to understand thoroughly the use of moisture and vapour barriers.

Another phenomenon which has become important in recent years – due to the increased use of impervious materials and sealed structures in building – is that of interstitial condensation. This is caused by changes in temperature acting on trapped construction water, and can cause eventual damage not only to finishes but to the structure itself. The likely extent of interstitial condensation can be predicted by graphical means (see Fig. 4.10) where the calculation shows that extensive condensation is likely, redesign to minimise the effect is essential.

Ventilation and air movement
The number of air changes required in a building relates much more to

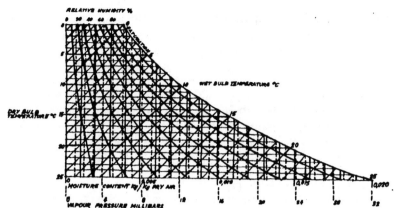

Fig. 4.9 The dewpoint can be predicted by relating humidity to temperature

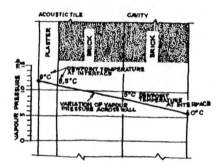

Fig. 4.10 The danger of interstitial condensation can be assessed by graphical means

avoiding a 'fuggy', smelly or oppresive atmosphere – excepting for specific and difficult conditions such as operating theatres or critical environments for manufacturing processes – than simply to providing the oxygen necessary to maintain life.

The aim is to provide a 'fresh' atmosphere without draughts, which means that both input and extraction must be carefully considered so that currents of air are controlled, and that control by occupants (though it may be psychologically desirable) may make optimum conditions difficult to achieve.

Special attention to precise ventilation requirements may be vital to remove bacteria, unpleasant fumes or excess heat in certain situations: in such cases, exact criteria will be provided by the client, and specialist advice will be essential – high priority will necessarily be attributed to specially onerous conditions of this kind, and other desirable conditions (quiet, perhaps) may have to be sacrificed.

Where full airconditioning is provided, either because especially high criteria have been established or in order that the arrangement of internal spaces can be free, specialist advice is essential.

Humidity and temperature can, in such conditions, be fully controlled through ventilation, but this demands sophisticated automatic controls, and unless failsafe backup systems are provided may result in the facilities being unusable in emergency. The desirability of allowing some autonomy over his own environmental conditions to the occupier – he will like to control not only temperature and light but the amount he is spending, too – should not be left out of any decision on the degree of artificiality to be incorporated into a building.

The barrier to the free circulation of air which is created by high buildings and the effect which they may have on ventilation, have been the subject of much study. In general, movements can be predicted, but any proposed building which is going to be prominent in its environment, or any group of buildings among which wind creation can be anticipated should be specially studied from this point of view. Quite small alterations of detail can have surprisingly large effects on air movement, and the removal of leading edges, for example, is often worthwhile.

Many departments of architecture or civil engineering have wind tunnels where they are pleased to subject scale models of buildings to smoke tests. These may reveal potential problems at a time when they can still be overcome.

The 'stack' effect of air, heated within a building, rising up within it must not be forgotten, and neither must the suction, or 'lift' which may be set up by wind movements and tend to raise roofs.

Light and insolation

There are generally no specific requirements governing the availability of sunlight in a building and today even the requirement for daylighting has in some cases been abandoned. We are, after all, perfectly happy in a theatre or a department store without windows, and in modern buildings the function of windows to provide a view is sometimes thought as important as their role in admitting light.

Most people, however, would regard daylighting as a necessity for habitable rooms (as opposed to workplaces). Many architects would think control of the levels of such lighting as an important facet of the aesthetic as well as the functional design. Objective levels required for the performance of many specific tasks have been established, but since these are normally expressed as percentages of light available from the unobstructed sky, the figures should be taken to apply only to climatic and geographical conditions analogous to our own. A reason for this expression as percentages is that glare due to violent differences in illumination of adjacent surfaces makes vision much more difficult than an overall low level of light, to which the eye adapts relatively much more easily.

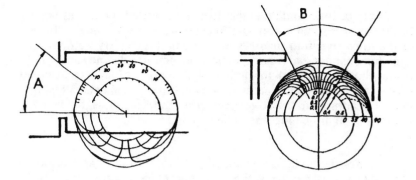

A × B ≃ SKY FACTOR

Fig. 4.11 Calculation of daylighting levels with BRE protractors

BRE sky component protractors (Fig. 4.11) are a more convenient method of estimating predicted daylighting levels than the Waldron diagram, but the latter may be required in more complicated situations.

The use of the protractors is easily commanded, if it is understood that (a) the droop inbuilt into the lines compensates for the varied brightness of the sky at different elevations above horizontal and (b) that the reading for each point on plan is obtained by multiplying a plan by a sectional reading. Thus while the sectional readings will be constant at all points on a line parallel to a window, the final readings will vary due to the different plan components.

It is best to plot the factors and interpolate 'contours' in order to obtain an immediate graphical presentation of the light distribution in the space.

Where more than one source of light illuminates the space, additional readings must be summed to obtain the full level for each point.

Detailed step-by-step instructions are supplied with the protractors, and the best way to become familiar with their use is by practice.

To obtain the very high sky factors recommended for, say, drawing offices (perhaps 5 per cent), may require very large windows in more than one plane – or else very narrow rooms. This is likely to increase heat loss, and it may be desirable in such a case to make very detailed calculations to establish whether artificial lighting of a suitable standard or high standards of thermal insulation would be most cost effective and economical of energy.

It is nowadays appreciated that solar gain from windows facing more or less due south can result in worthwhile savings in energy consumption if it is exploited and controlled. It should be noted, though, that unwanted solar gain can make rooms virtually unusable in summer unless efficient (probably outside) shading is provided.

Many people would feel that to sit in a shaded room overlooking a sunlit landscape had advantages in comparison with sitting in the glare of the sun gazing into shadows. Because in this country we rarely get a truly hot summer, we can forget how uncomfortable one can be to those who have to work through it. Where precautions such as inbuilt brises-soleil can be incorporated in a building, this may be a highly desirable adjunct to the large areas of south-facing glass that would be effective if solar heating was to be exploited.

Heat

It is rare for the building envelope itself (apart from solar gain) to be utilised as a source of heat, though a theoretical structure that would react to external conditions by varying heat input from circulating pipes (on an almost biological pattern) has been hypothesised.

The thermal capacity, or ability of a structure to retain and store heat, is an important aspect of the heat characteristics of a building, however: a building which retains heat, which will be released over a considerable period of time may save energy by permitting cheap 'off peak' fuel to be used, but the necessity to predict future temperatures when deciding how much heat to store makes this a very blunt and unresponsive facility.

Obtaining the optimum temperature demands consideration of many aspects of heat balance, and will normally be a matter for a consultant – he will be aided if the initial designers have been aware of factors of the kind referred to above which will affect the behaviour of the system.

The envelope is more commonly considered as a controller of heat loss, and U-value calculations leading to overall calculations of heat loss – and thus to an assessment of the heat input required – are normally made. This is a technique that should be familiar to every architectural technician.

U-values are a measure of the rate at which heat escapes through a particular sandwich of materials, so that the lower the figure is, the better the insulation being obtained.

From published values of conductivity (k) the resistivity ($1/k$) can be obtained. The resistance of each layer of material in the sandwich is then calculated by multiplying thickness by resistivity. By adding together the resistances, (including the resistances of surfaces and cavities) and taking the reciprocal of the total, U is obtained.

Overall U-values of many common constructions are published, and the effect of a change in one material, the omission of a layer, or the addition of extra material can easily be calculated by adaptation of the method referred to above. The reciprocal of the U-value is taken to give the sum of the resistances, which can suitably be adjusted before the reciprocal is taken again to obtain U.

The Building Regulation requirements for insulation standards are an excellent guide, but should be thought of as minimum rather than

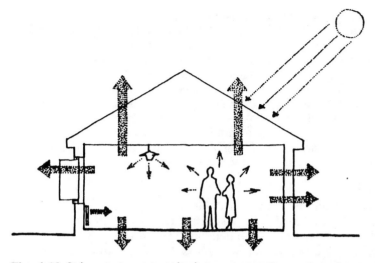

Fig. 4.12 It is necessary to take into account many more factors than
U-value, to establish the thermal characteristics of a building

optimum standards. Far lower U-values can be obtained, and are likely
to pay for themselves in energy savings.

U-values in themselves have only a limited significance, however.
The total heat loss from a building is of more importance, and this is
obtained by multiplying the U-value of each part of the structure
(window, wall, floor, roof and so on) by its superficial area. Even so,
losses other than through the structure have to be considered.

Several buildings have been constructed which can normally
operate without heat input from plant, relying on the heat from
lighting, machines and occupants coupled with excellent thermal
insulation. In at least one case this was found perfectly satisfactory
except for the period immediately following an extended
Christmas/New Year break, and special arrangements have had to be
made.

To design a building to work in this way, understanding of the
'admittance' method of calculation is necessary. This depends upon
additional sophistication of overall heat loss calculations, to take into
account the behaviour of a building throughout a twenty-four hour
period, balancing heat loss against input, including the input from
external sources. If a subtle balance of this kind is required it is
essential to have the early advice of an experienced engineer, and to
accept the inevitable constraints that will be imposed on window size.

It must not be forgotten that the type of insulation which depends
on creating a layer of still air by the use of materials containing air
pockets (for example, expanded polystyrene, fibreglass quilt or sealed
double glazing) is a barrier basically only to conducted heat. It
is necessary also to prevent the migration of radiated heat (by

reflection – incorporation of layers of reflective materials, such as metal-faced boards) and of convected heat by discouraging air loss (by draught-stopping and avoidance of flue effects).

Care has to be taken not to jeopardise waterproofing in the search for high standards of thermal insulation. Where suspended ground floors are abandoned in favour of the better insulability of solid ones, damp proof membranes will usually be necessary: where cavities in brickwork are filled with foam to improve U-values, great care is needed to avoid providing a path for water migration across the cavity. It is doubtful whether the filling of cavities in existing properties can be unreservedly recommended, for this reason.

Sound

The general noisiness of life, with jets and juggernauts, has undoubtedly increased in the last generation, and with it the need to exclude unwanted noise from buildings. This may be difficult to reconcile with other demands – such as that for natural ventilation – and an assessment of priorities is generally called for.

It should be remembered, too, that sound generated within a building may need to be kept in, and that transmission of sound from one cell to another within the building may require control.

For these aims to be achieved demands understanding of the two ways in which sound is transmitted – through the structure and through the air – so that the paths it may take can be traced and interrupted.

Sound which is structure-borne is most effectively blocked by a positive break in the structure, as is shown in the floor detail in Fig. 4.13. An alternative is to make the structure so heavy that it will not vibrate and so pass sound on, but this may be a prohibitively expensive expedient in modern buildings.

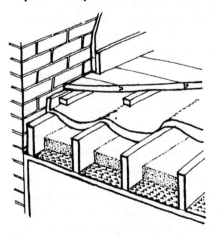

Fig. 4.13 If the transmission of sound is to be prevented, the two structures must be totally divorced from one another

Airborne sound will pass through any gaps – even the small ones around the opening lights of a window – and can be difficult to stop. Double-glazed windows which are to reduce sound transmission must be closed to be effective. They should also have large gaps between two independent frames, and the reveals can be lined with sound-absorbent material to further reduce transmission.

Sound can also be damped at source by the use of absorbent materials, which may save expensive remedies further from the point of origin, and the design of spaces should be considered to ensure that no sympathetic vibrations are set up.

Control of the quality of sound within a room depends on the reverberation periods at a variety of frequencies, as well as the placing of absorbents to avoid echoes and the shaping of the space to ensure appropriate sound distribution – a process analagous to the placing of mirrors to diffuse or focus a light.

Physical integrity

It is impossible to design buildings to be used indefinitely, even if that were thought desirable. All building materials deteriorate eventually, and the cost of maintenance becomes prohibitive.

In any case, our needs from buildings and the demands in terms of performance standards that we make of them, change quite rapidly. As a new facility or a new level of performance becomes practicable and economic, so it ceases to be an exceptional luxury and is demanded of all buildings, and older ones rapidly become obsolete. As a result, it is quite normal to think of buildings as having a life of seventy years or even less – the predicted life should be part of the briefing before design begins. Ideally, no doubt, the whole thing would quietly crumble at the end of its allotted span.

The aim, though, is a building that will require as little maintenance as possible during its planned life. This will, of course, be balanced against first cost, on terotechnological lines (see Ch. 12). Materials and assemblies have to be selected so that the amount of time, materials and labour expended in maintenance is minimised. For example, the choice between hardwood or softwood for joinery may involve assessment of the maintenance needs of each during fifty years. If it is anticipated that the life of plant will be shorter than that of the building it serves, access for replacement will be needed, which would be unnecessary if plant which would last as long as the building could be built in. Another example is the need to replace windows. With some types of double-glazing, the whole unit has to be replaced if there is a breakage, rather than the pane. This is not only expensive in itself, but demands that the cladding should be so designed to allow removal and replacement without extensive dismantling.

The materials selected must be ones which, subject to conscientious maintenance by the occupiers of the building, will not show serious deterioration during the building's life. Where finishes .

are concerned the alternative strategy of making allowance for replacement at necessary intervals may be preferred because it permits updating, even if life-cycle costing indicates that this is the more expensive option.

It is impossible to achieve a building in which every part will need replacement at the same time, but the desirability of this aim must none the less be remembered.

An understanding of the basic characteristics of the materials being selected, and their likely behaviour under changes of temperature, humidity and load is necessary if intelligent choices are to be made. The accumulated wisdom of generations as encapsulated in the local vernacular of design may be a useful guide (and no doubt buildings following it will fit into their surroundings well) but it is not always practicable or desirable to follow such entrenched practice. Fresh thought to the particular exposure, air pollution and soil conditions and special loading conditions, is desirable. What is right in London may be wrong on a cliff-top in Scotland, and vice versa.

An additional facet of the question of physical integrity is the fireproofing and protection of buildings. The Building Regulations do, of course, pay very considerable attention to this aspect of design, and the advice of the local fire prevention officer is freely available on the design of escapes and the provision of fire-fighting equipment.

Architectural expression

It is still important that buildings should convey a message about their owners, their occupants and their use.

I am not now discussing aesthetics so much as the characteristics which make us instinctively recognise that a building is recreational or industrial, that it is a church or a house. These characteristics are easy to recognise but hard to define: they seem to stem from honest expression on the exterior of a building of the nature of the interior, so that a large single space is expressed quite differently from a series of small ones, and an intricate plan is evident from the exterior (Figs. 4.14, 4.15).

Certainly this has nothing to do with the adoption of 'appropriate' decorative motifs: these are an irrelevance – some would say an admission of defeat – and would be unnecessary if the design was really first-class.

This honest statement of the organic nature of the building should be echoed by an equivalent truth to the form of construction, so that reinforced concrete does not ape stone forms, nor rendered brick masquerade as concrete. If these principles are followed, there should be no need for any contrived architectonic form: the building will speak clearly to users, will be straightforward to use, and will induce an appropriate mood – and create pride in the occupants.

Additionally, the building will be part of the environment of many people who will never have occasion to enter it. It must provide a

Fig. 4.14 Expression of a single cell interior

Fig. 4.15 Expression of a cellular interior

suitable element in the townscape, without undue intrusion, and integrate into its surroundings. Individuality without eccentricity is required for this reason of the great majority of buildings. It is only the very occasional site or function that can justify a 'prima donna' design which demands attention.

Safety from invasion

The demands of security from burglary, vandalism and other enemies is obviously of great importance to occupiers. Considerable advice is freely available to designers from the insurance companies and the police, and should be carefully considered: they will advise on the choice and siting of locks, bolts and alarms, as well as the lighting of approaches and such obvious (but easily overlooked) points as avoiding footholds up the ashlar for cat-burglars.

Avoidance of actual industrial espionage may be essential in some circumstances. Neither banks nor prisons want details of their locks and security procedures widely known, and elaborate precautions may be demanded to preserve confidentiality. Expert advice would usually be provided from the organisation's own specialists.

Privacy

In our modern, high-density towns adequate privacy can be difficult to attain. Everyone, however, has the need for some degree of solitude, and many people find it virtually impossible to undertake any task demanding concentration surrounded by even subdued activity. On the other hand, others may be stimulated by the interactions due to shared workplaces. Protection at some time or other from overlooking (and overhearing) is a necessity in the majority of situations.

Not only is this protection necessary, we need also to be protected from the intrusion which being forced to overlook or overhear entails. Both visual stops and acoustic controls need subtle calculation if an acceptable balance is to be achieved, so that everyone can function to capacity.

In the domestic situation, where one hopes to relax, privacy may be felt to be of even greater importance. This may be both privacy between, and privacy within, dwellings. We neither wish to have sights intruded upon us nor to be watched; neither to have our neighbours radio intruded upon us nor to have them listen to our inevitable family disagreements.

Plan arrangement can do a great deal to preserve the integrity of each home, even in a very high-density scheme, like the one shown in Fig. 4.16. Cutting-off paths of vision alone may be insufficient if sound is still allowed to pass unhindered, and heavy walls to give a minimum of perhaps 45 dB sound reduction between dwellings will need to be accompanied by attention to reduce the passage of airborne sound. Windows designed to prevent the passage of sound will be effective only while they are closed, so that in a particularly difficult situation artificial ventilation may be an expensive necessity (see 'Sound' p. 70).

Fig. 4.16 High density need not preclude privacy, if the design is carefully thought out

Buildability

Any designer who is overconscious of the need for his conception to be buildable will find his imagination trammelled by that requirement. His designs are likely to be pedestrian. On the other hand, it is clearly pointless to produce beautiful fantasies which are incapable of realisation. The building must be got up – though understanding of the general principles of statics may ensure that this requirement is met more effectively than overadherence to a particular system, in the earliest stages of design at least (see, however, Ch. 5).

While sensible use of the resources of time and money will demand understanding of the potential capabilities of the industry, the design team should not feel bound to select the cheapest or quickest method of construction. There may often be occasions when an alternative is more suitable. The convenience of the builder is not a predominant criterion of good building design.

Structural stability

Given determination, even the most apparently unstable structures can be satisfactorily built, but there need to be clear reasons for this to be acceptable – not least because most observers find such structures unpleasantly disconcerting. If there is any doubt about the likely stability of a structure balanced on a small bearing, oddly angled, or of otherwise unconventional structural design, a structural engineer will obviously be brought into the design team from a very early stage. Clearly, every building must in fact be stable, whether it looks it or not, fantasy may have to give way to sense on occasion.

The most effectively startling structures are often those that exploit newly developed structural design methods, as was the case both with the vaulting of the fifteenth century (Fig. 4.17) and the shell concrete structures of the mid-twentieth (see Ch. 5).

The use of published data

In the areas of anthropometrics, thermal and sound insulation, daylighting and most other technical fields, there is a body of data published. Government departments and individual publishers also provide useful compilations of collected experience of convenient solutions to particular problems of planning and detailed design. These bulletins and source books make a convenient jumping-off point for the solution of individual problems: it is important that they should be available, and consulted – but also that they should be treated as what they are. That is to say, they give generalised guidance which may not necessarily apply to every case. They indicate which considerations are most likely to be significant to the design of a particular building type, or the solution of a particular functional problem.

On environmental questions there is continuous research, and it is

Fig. 4.17 The most effective design is often the one that uses a novel structure to the full

important to keep abreast of the digests put out by the Building Research Establishment. Methods are devised and evaluated for establishing satisfactory lighting, thermal or acoustic design, for example, which lead to an apparently endless raising of standards.

Everyone in the design team, not just the specialists most concerned, should be aware of this progress, which may point to quite simple changes in detail design which can have apparently disproportionate practical advantages. For example, a new window section may have a significant effect on daylight distribution without additional expense.

Members of the design team should also be familiar with the use of the abstracts put out by the The British Architectural Library (BAL), which list by subject every relevant publication received by the library. Copies or photocopies of such material can be obtained through public libraries' interlibraries loans services, so giving access to published material from worldwide sources.

Generalised books of 'architects' data' have their place in the office library. They cover a wide field, and are easy to refer to – provided they are used as guides and not as crutches.

The principal danger in relying on published sources is that information (because it appears in printed form) may be given undue authority. The wise member of a design team never relies on what he reads if experience, training and commonsense lead him to a different conclusion.

The design specification

It is possible, and often highly desirable, to draw up a detailed functional specification which sets out the mandatory and preferred requirements for each activity to be accommodated.

Objective criteria can be established, on the lines of those published in the *CIB Master List of Properties* on the basis of the overall requirements and priorities established. For example, if even daylighting equal to a 2 per cent sky factor is required over 80 per cent of the floor area, or if sound insulation equal to 50 dB is needed between two spaces, this can be laid down as a clearly understood requirement. Neither of these requirements presupposes a particular solution – in the first case a north light roof might be an alternative to windows, and in the second the rooms could be physically separated by a store instead of having a single heavy wall between them.

This demonstrates the vital point – at this stage criteria of design are being laid down, the solution has not been attempted. The approach to design which can see only one possible solution to each problem stultifies imagination and progress, and is to be avoided.

It is unfortunately common for designers to abandon the attempt to attain standards because they have never seen them achieved and believe it is impossible. Every new standard is at some point achieved for the first time. We should always be prepared to make the attempt.

In the case of the factory introduced in Chapter 2, the standards required might be those shown on the chart (Fig. 4.18). The stars indicate the levels regarded as having priority.

Performance criteria for many of the finishes to be selected are shown on the same chart.

Summary

While any designer will be clearly aware of the whole spectrum of functional constraints – and will be made aware, quite sharply, by occupiers of his building of any failure in any of these respects – he will know that not every optimum standard can be fully achieved. The conditions of the individual problem will help him (in consultation with the client) to define the priorities and the acceptable compromises. He will rarely design a building for perfection in one particular respect – a balance will generally be the aim.

| Factory at | | | | | | Performance standards |
Accommodation	Temp (°C)	Ventilation (air changes/h)	Natural light (sky factor)	Artificial light (lux)	Sound control	Other
Goods & Materials	13	1	0.5%	100	—	Humidity 20 - 50% *
Public Areas	16	1	1%	100	—	—
Admin. Areas	20	1	2%	400	—	—
Workshops	16	22.6 m³ per person	* 5%	* 600	60 db reduction	Humidity 20 - 50% *
Toilets	18	2	0.5%	100	—	—

* INDICATES CRITICAL

Fig. 4.18 It is convenient to set out the detailed performance requirements of the building in chart form

It may often fall to the architectural technician to explore and evaluate the consequences of more-or-less stringent functional requirements, so as to provide a suitable context for decisions. The technician should familiarise himself in practise with the techniques referred to in this chapter, the technical basis of which will be familiar to him from his study of technology. There is no room in a book of this kind to do more than mention such methods and their importance, and students should refer to textbooks on environmental design for detailed treatment, and to the standard textbooks on construction for the methods by which established criteria can be attained.

Chapter 5

Technical constraints

The origins, characteristics and manufacture of the materials used in construction make up an expressive vocabulary. The forms of construction are the grammar with which they are put together to make meaningful wholes. Exactly as language may be quite correctly and properly used in a government memorandum, evocatively employed by a skilled journalist or become the vehicle used by a poet to express his philosophy, so the vocabulary and syntax of construction can be employed either to produce utilitarian structures which are aesthetically pedestrian, a pleasant though unremarkable built environment, or great works of architecture.

If the designer is to achieve either of these latter aims, he needs (like the journalist or poet) to understand not only the 'correct' use of his raw materials, but also sympathetic appreciation of its qualities, associations and overtones so that he can put materials together sensitively to say what he intends. This demands familiarity with the range of options that are open to him, so that he understands the strengths and limitations of each material and element and can foresee the effect any combination is likely to produce. Each material needs to be selected thoughtfully, used to do the job for which it is most appropriate and be fully and honestly expressed in the total building. This does not mean, of course, that the shock effect of an occasional discord must be entirely eschewed: in poetry it is frequently the unexpected analogy which illuminates the writer's message. The designer of buildings need not feel he must always follow well trodden paths just because the methods in question are familiar and known to 'work'. What is important is that he should work consciously. If he decides (say) to appear to support a heavy load on a single slender post he must understand the effect that will be created and be sure in his own mind that his choice is valid and justifiable.

Materials

It is not possible, here, to examine the characteristics of all the materials and constructional forms available to the designer. They will, in any case, be familiar to the reader.

The principle to be established is the need to examine every constructional expedient critically: to look again at the ways in which familiar forms are used. Could there be an alternative better-suited to the purpose? Are there any disadvantages to choosing the proposed detail? Are the characteristics of the material fully exploited?

For example, it might be necessary to decide between the use of brickwork and that of exposed aggregate concrete cladding panels for the external skin of a reinforced-concrete-framed building. Either would be a suitable and acceptable choice, from a functional point of view, and the load imposed on the frame would not be very different. Brickwork which passes a reinforced concrete frame, however, tends to show pattern staining and can be 'pushed' by differential thermal movement. It is also more difficult to fix: the sensible detail if brickwork is chosen may be to inset the cladding within an exposed frame. Exposed aggregate panels, on the other hand, can readily be suspended as storey-height units from the frame, which they can conceal. This limits the number of joints to be sealed. Both materials can be used, at a pinch, in either way, but the designer should take into account the simplest, most straightforward, and, in the long run, most satisfactory way of using each, and accept the visual implications of the choice he makes. If each material is understood and used sympathetically, the overall effect is right and the unease that may subconsciously worry an observer if a material is asked to do something outside its normal capacity is avoided.

The case I have quoted is a subtle and evenly balanced one. The designer will have aesthetic aims which may tip the balance one way or the other. He ought to avoid the temptation, though, to use one material in imitation of the other. If one material is the right and justifiable choice, can the building not make an honest statement of that fact?

Brickwork is a most flexible and resourceful material, and so familiar a part of our everyday environment that we often fail to consider its impact fully. Many sensitive designers, though, prefer to differentiate quite sharply between the way they use bricks structurally and the way they are expressed when they are only a cladding. They may use continuous vertical joint or bricks on end in cladding, and elaborate bondings in structural walls, for example.

The designer's aim, almost always, will be to produce an unworrying, even an unobtrusive, background to life, and he will rarely have the conscious wish to make the occupant or passer-by uneasy in any way (though, of course, there can be occasions for deliberate shock, as baroque architecture demonstrates). He should also aim to reveal the best characteristics of each material he uses. Every material has these, though thought is sometimes needed to remind ourselves of what they are: the texture of brick, the colour of natural stone, the glitter of glass, perhaps. We might aim to reveal and enjoy the grain of timber rather than asking the joiner to make it into a neat copy of the smooth face of plastic, and enjoy the perfection of a plastic surface, emphasising it with colour and pattern rather than concealing it under a poor imitation of wood grain. In the same way, anyone using concrete as a loadbearing material should have the confidence to let this be apparent. What other material has the masculinity of mass concrete? The aggregate can be exposed to provide colour, or the surface boardmarked to give texture, but it is an admission of defeat to disguise the concrete to look like ashlar. If a smooth finish is wanted, of course, there is nothing false about applying one, so long as this is, quite evidently, only a surface finish. It ought not to be jointed after the fashion of a Florentine palazzo when the underlying construction is totally different.

Structural form

In the same way in which it is good to let materials express their own personalities, so the constraints imposed by the choice of a particular constructional method have to be accepted and used by the designer. It is more productive to exploit the opportunity offered by a particular way of putting materials together than to try to fight the natural character of those systems. No doubt a gardener could dwarf hollyhocks and grow giant pansies if he wanted to – with an enormous amount of labour. The result would certainly be remarkable and would draw surprised comment. A garden where plants grow to their natural size in the conditions which suit them best is both an easier one to care for and a pleasanter one to visit.

Steel frames and reinforced concrete can be made to do a great deal: their capabilities sometimes seem endless. They are used most elegantly (in the scientists' sense of the term) when they are used in a simple and straightforward fashion to do a job to which they are well suited.

Civil engineers often seem to understand this better than the designers of many buildings. The design of bridges is generally a clear expression of the chosen structure. This is true, of course, of the best buildings, and should be true of them all.

Trabeated construction

Post and beam construction has been used from very early times and though it is one of the simplest possible constructional methods it can result in buildings of great sophistication. Figure 5.1 shows an ancient Greek temple where the simple placing of load on beam, beam on column and column on base has been underlined by the delicate modelling of the elèments by fluting, mouldings and carved capitals so that a unified and eminently satisfying design is produced. This design is a direct statement of structure, modified only by the aesthetic sensibility of the designer. He has not asked more of the post and beam than they can readily achieve, but has been content to accept the limitations imposed by their use.

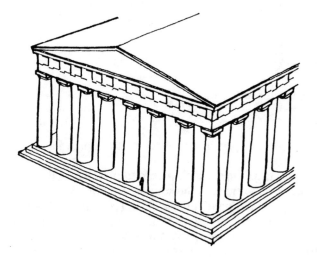

Fig. 5.1 Beam, post and lintol generate rectilinear forms

Post and beam could also, of course, result in a crude and unmemorable building if proportion, dynamic and unity were unconsidered: letting the structure speak for itself is not a magic formula guaranteeing successful design – but success is made difficult to achieve if structural honesty is ignored. If an attempt was made to produce a circular building by such means (and it's not unheard of) the technical devices needed would complicate the building and make success less likely. Junctions between beams of varying depth can make messy column heads, beams at other than right angles to one another can result in unfortunately complicated fixings.

It is necessary in trabeated construction to accept the limitations of span imposed by the available materials – stone sizes or tree heights.

The practice of concealing lintols behind apparently unsupported structures is common but needs careful justification. The appearance of a stretcher course of bricks carrying a wall, or a load carried on a window frame can be unsettling even to the uninformed observer. Many designers would prefer at least to show a lintol toe or a soldier arch as a slight acknowledgement of the need for support.

Fig. 5.2 Domes demand squares on plan

Dome
The use of a dome to roof a space generally demands a plan based upon the square.

The spaces around the dome, which is carried directly on the crowns of four arches on the sides of the square, are filled with segments of spheres known as pendentives which transmit the load from the remainder of the circumference to the arches. Since it is important for the loading to be even, a symmetrical arrangement is virtually mandatory. This produces a most distinctive architectural mass, which would be hard to disguise but which can be exploited. This has been done outstandingly at Santa Sophia (Fig. 5.2) to create a monumental and unified statement.

Arcuated construction
The invention of the arch, using small elements to span wide spaces, and doing so by creating a mechanism which becomes stronger when loaded, released building from the limitations of the beam. The result was the domed structures mentioned above, and the barrel vault which roofed a rectangular space with a whole series of arches. Cross-vaults could be used over square plans, allowing good headroom. The invention of the pointed arch allowed rectangular spaces to be cross-vaulted, with an even ridge line, and gave new flexibility to planners.

The Romans used only the semicircular arch. With this a barrel vault is possible, but a cross-vault can only sensibly be produced over a square plan. Mediaeval ribbed vaulting seems to have been borne of

Fig. 5.3 Exploitation of the arch gives a distinctive character to the building

the realisation of the saving that could be made in centering, if a skeleton of arches could be constructed in advance of the vault surfaces, leaving these to be filled in segment by segment. The intelligent response of a constructor!

If one considers a square cross-vault, one soon realises that if the barrels from which it is made are semicircular, the diagonal ribs will be elliptical – and hard to build. The inspiration which solved this problem opened the door to the stunning engineering of the Middle Ages: it was realised that with pointed arches one could have arches over many different spans all reaching the same height, and all would be made from segments of circles. Figure 5.3 shows how the potential of this system was exploited to give light, airy and elegant buildings.

The appearance of such buildings is a very direct expression of the engineering system adopted, which developed out of the needs of the men who constructed them.

This is not discussed because much gothic vaulting is likely to be called for today! It is, however, an excellent example of the importance of technological considerations to successful design.

Frame

The framed multi-storey building has become a basic building unit of our time, to the extent that we may take this method of construction very much for granted. Unlike the gothic builders, who learned their building empirically, we can predict success and design to fine limits. None-the-less, experiment on occasion still leads to failure, and many designers wish to play safe by adopting only well-tried strategies. This need not mean (as it so often does) that buildings need to be dully repetitive. Wide spans and towering spires are known to work, we can lift a building off the ground to 'float' on pilotis if we wish, or we can cantilever large structures from central stems. We do not have to take risks structurally to produce adventurous design.

What can and what should be done are not, of course, always the same thing. We may know we can omit columns, make holes through buildings or create irregular forms if we wish: is it desirable?

It is basic to the loadbearing frame that it will have a simple repetitive grid, that loads will be transmitted in as direct a manner as possible and that no unnecessary structural weight will be added. There are great advantages if column and beam sizes can be standardised (both from the point of view of simple construction and that of appearance). Of course, there will be times when such rules are broken to good advantage – but this will be a matter of conscious choice, it should never be done arbitrarily.

The selection of the structural grid is generally critical to the success of such buildings, and is influenced by both functional and constructional factors.

Once this grid has been chosen, it becomes a basic condition of the design and should only be departed from for the strongest of reasons. For example, if a constructional grid of 3 m × 10 m has been chosen because this permits the use of a standard prefabricated deck unit and allows double-banked offices to be well lit naturally, if a large space is required beyond what can be enclosed in one bay (perhaps for a refectory) it has to be accepted that this will be interrupted by free-standing columns. If, on the other hand, such columns are clearly unacceptable – if instead of a refectory it is an auditorium that is in question – then that part of the accommodation ought to be arranged in a separate block. It is not appropriate to try to fit it in to the gridded one. The one option that should only be considered in extreme circumstances is that of inserting heavy beams to allow a wide uninterrupted span at one point, and thus compromise the simplicity of every lower floor.

Loadbearing brick

Brickwork is such a familiar part of the built environment that we are liable to fail to examine the ways in which we use it as rigorously as perhaps we should. The small, standardised unit of burnt clay which can carry such loads in compression, can make rectilinear or curved forms and weathers so well, has its own limitations.

Firstly, of course, it is weak in tension, and should not be expected to support tensile stresses or to appear to do so. Though brickwork can be reinforced, the occasions when this expedient is to be preferred to reinforced concrete are limited.

Secondly, considerable skill is required to produce brickwork which is at once sound and good looking, and such skill is becoming rarer.

Thirdly, though the colour and texture of brickwork varies a good deal, the effect of its repetition over large areas can seem dull and characterless, though if the design is lively it may impose a welcome unity.

If these limitations are consciously accepted by the designer he has the best chance of producing a good result. Brickwork should look stable – arches rather than concealed lintols will give this effect, and so will fat piers rather than over-slender ones. If the size of the brick can be accepted as a design module, so that the cutting of bricks is eliminated, this is advantageous, and decorative brickwork should exploit the natural texture and shape of the brick rather than fight it.

Cross-wall construction, as shown in Fig. 5.4 imposes its own constraints. The number of openings through the structural walls must be limited, and the walls need to be buttressed. Adherence to such rules not only improves technical performance but enhances appearance as well.

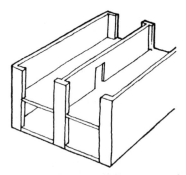

Fig. 5.4 Cross-wall construction imposes firm discipline on design

Shell concrete

Shell concrete has much in common with the domed and vaulted structures discussed earlier. Clearly the structural design is so critical in such a case that few would argue that the demands it imposes must be met. The visual strength of such a form is generally so strong as to be the inevitable focus of interest, and all other forms must be treated as subsidiary.

Once the bay size has been established, or the overall size of the stadium or theatre determined, this can only be changed by returning completely to the earliest design stage. In many cases, however, it is far easier to alter the actual positions of supports than is the case with framed structures.

There are severe limitations on the extent to which the shell can be perforated (Fig. 5.5).

Many shell-concrete constructions depend almost entirely for their effect on expression of the naked shell, which is basically a very simple

88

Fig. 5.5 The plan forms that can be roofed with shell concrete are strongly geometric

geometric form. This works splendidly provided the initial shape is determined by someone with both knowledge of structures and a sensitive eye. There is a danger that designers with a less sophisticated understanding of structures will produce sketches of shapes which are pseudo-structural but can be virtually impossible to calculate or build. This is an inverted approach. One must be prepared to accept and express the mathematically optimum form rather than assume that this splendid material has limitless capabilities.

Pneumatic structures
Inflated structures that depend either on a slight differential pressure between internal and external air pressure, or on the inflation to a high pressure of integral ribs, may become of increasing importance. Although at present these are generally only employed as temporary buildings (a use to which their demountability and light weight eminently suits them) this may not always be the case. We should note that the choice of such a building will at once impose a simple shape and rounded forms on the design.

Geodesic dome
The dome made up from a light structural network with infill panels depends upon the load being spread through all the parts and must therefore be treated with respect. The structure is as exposed, and the shape as predetermined, as those of the gothic cathedral (Fig. 5.6).

Constructional factors
The word 'construction' seems to be used nowadays in our industry in two rather different (though related) ways. This is, of course, a gross

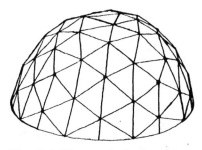

Fig. 5.6 The geodesic dome leaves little room for variation in the design

oversimplification of the ways in which language is used, and the many senses and overtones any word can acquire in use, but perhaps I can explain what I mean in this instance if I suggest that the first meaning which springs to the mind of a designer is the concept of the assembled materials as they will remain throughout the life of the building, while to the builder the principal implication is of the actual process of assembling those materials, the way in which the building is put together initially. So to a builder 'construction' has a great deal to do with labour and plant while to the architect it is concerned with the interactions between materials and joints that will move without leaking, and so on.

In this section, I am using the term in the constructor's sense. The availability of materials and skilled labour, the influence of plant on site operations, and the need to transport components, all have a relevance to design which designers are too ready to overlook.

The desirability and practicability of involving the builder in the design process are discussed in Ch. 1. The expertise in current site organisation and the availability and relative cost of materials and processes can only effectively come from someone in intimate day-to-day contact with the construction process.

Skill and craftsmanship

It is common for the designer to be aware that a process is possible without fully appreciating the degree of skill involved. A local authority team was some years ago set the task of designing houses for a self-build group who were completely without craft skills. These architects, therefore, set out to design convenient, attractive dwellings which were very simple indeed to put up. There were to be a minimum of cut bricks, and no openings through brick walls, for example, the simple stair was arranged so that only the simplest trimming of joists was required, and so on. A very attractive design was produced: the analytical thought that went into the exercise paid off in appearance and economy (though sad to relate, the client group found the appearance unconventional and opted for a more 'ordinary' house type! The design would actually not look out of the ordinary today, however. As has been remarked, designers' taste isn't so much different from that of the public as ahead of it.)

A similar situation might arise if a design is to be implemented in a developing country of the Third World, where skill will be at a premium though unskilled labour may be readily available. The levels of skill and craftsmanship which can be tapped, and their relative costs, are very relevant to intelligent design.

On the other hand, designers may sometimes justifiably be accused of discouraging the acquisition of high craft skills, since they give little or no opportunity for their exercise. Too many craftsmen do their best work as test pieces, only to spend a working lifetime on mundane and simple jobs. Of course, the bricklayer who can build a rubbed arch is likely to build a presentable wall, but there is a good case for inviting his cooperation in devising a door surround or a fireplace.

As, unfortunately, the craftsman's level of design rarely matches his skill, he can hardly be left to devise such features alone, but if his skills are understood by the designers, they can be used to the advantage of the building, and the craftsman will be encouraged.

The constructional process

The designer should also try to understand the actual methods the builder will employ to put his ideas into effect, though it is not his job to dictate what those methods should be. How much elbow room and manoeuvring space will be needed? In what order will the work be completed? At which stages will the weather be critical?

It may help the builder (and keep costs down) if the building is arranged so that the roof can be completed before intermediate floors, so that the building can be sealed at an early stage, or if (in a sprawling two or three-storey construction) earth ramps can be put in temporarily so that materials can be delivered by truck.

Alternatively, the builder may welcome the chance to cover, and even heat, the site, to facilitate continuous work (Fig. 5.7). It is

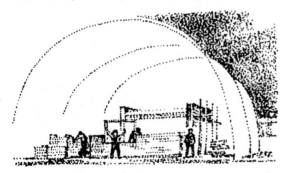

Fig. 5.7 The builder may welcome the opportunity to cover his site from inclement weather

possible that some detail of the design may prevent this, and that this could have been avoided if the point had been considered at an early enough stage.

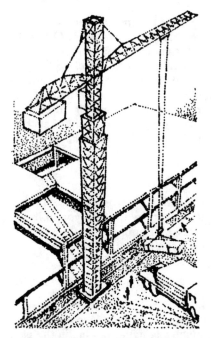

Fig. 5.8 The capabilities of plant may affect the practicability of a design solution

Handling and plant

It is also important for designers to appreciate the limitations and capabilities of the plant – cranes, concrete-mixing plant, pick-ups, earthmoving equipment and so on – which may be available to the contractor (Fig. 5.8).

The maximum loads of such equipment, the relationship between reach and load in the case of cranes, and the working space they require can affect the cost of a job seriously. I know of one building, at least, where the additional load of some extra-large cladding panels which had to be got up at the extremity of a crane's reach necessitated the importation of an additional plant for a short period. This could have been avoided if the problem had been understood – the panels could have been subdivided.

It should be noted that our contractual system works against a rational approach to such problems. If the difficulty was not realised when the builder tendered, he is deemed, none the less, to have included it in his price for the whole of the job. He finds he isn't entitled to an 'extra' for doing a job that was included in the original documents, even if it was only implicit there. There is no reason for the designer to alter his design simply for the convenience of the builder at that stage.

The delivery of such panels, storage, safe lifting and securing in position are of course the entire responsibility of the builder. Often the difficulties involved could be eased by designers if they were aware they were liable to occur and aimed to plan them out. Much of the unnecessary friction between designer and constructor arises because, (although not unaware of such problems) designers regard them as outside their terms of reference, and can see no financial or other advantage to the client. However rigorous the attention paid to such aspects by the architect, would the builder actually reduce his price because this had been the case?

Safety

The builder has far-reaching responsibilities to his workpeople, the eventual occupants of the building and passers-by for safety, and he may be helped to discharge this if the designer appreciates the requirements and the ways in which they can be met. Chapter 13 includes more information in this respect.

Non-prefabricated system building

There is an increasing number of builders who will make available a fully detailed constructional system, much as might be done in the case of a prefabricated system, which they offer as a basis for the design of a variety of buildings. The constraints of such a system are known to the designer,and the builder has all the advantages of optimum efficiency. The architect is limited by the limited range of options made available, and tied to a particular contractor, exactly as in the case of a prefabricated system, but the advantages of constructional efficiency should in this case be passed on to the client.

Relative importance

The eventual functioning of the building throughout its life will always, it goes without saying, be more important than the efficiency and ease with which it was erected. There is an interaction, however.

If the building can be put up quickly it ought to be cheaper. This may mean that the owner can afford either a bigger building or a better-quality one, which in either case will affect his enjoyment of the building, or he may have a lower debt to pay off. So the advantages of efficiency are not only with the builder.

Services

Very early decisions which are made with regard to service installations in a building commonly have far-reaching effects. It is important that such consequences should be fully understood when the advice of specialists is weighed and decisions are taken. The easiest path at such a time is to listen to the reasoned arguments (or even the bald advice) of the specialist uncritically, and to accept it without great thought. The specialist is seeing the problem in isolation – it is up to the architect to put it into context, to see the results which may be consequent upon the choice and to come to a decision which may not be the optimum for the service or installation in question but will be the best for the building as a whole. For this, he must be properly informed not only on specialist matters, but on the relationships between the different aspects of the building.

Choice of fuel

The nature of fuel storage, the provision of flues, and the positioning of plant rooms may be profoundly affected by choice of fuel. If gas is selected, no store will be required, nor will automatic stokers or a heavy flue, in many cases. The plant room can go virtually anywhere, provided there is reasonable access to change the boiler when necessary, and need not occupy valuable ground-floor space. These advantages may be sufficient to offset the additional cost compared to solid fuel.

If solid fuel is chosen, more stringent constraints will be imposed.

A large fuel store, with road access for delivery lorries will have to occupy a prime section of the building. There will often be automatic stokers, and therefore a critical relationship between store and plant room, and provision for the storage and removal of ash. A heavy and obtrusive flue will be needed.

Add to this the additional work for a caretaker or maintenance man, and the need for dangerous and heavy lorries to enter the site regularly, and the choice of fuel is clearly concerned with more than cost.

Distribution of services

The cost, as well as the efficiency in use, of the services will be greatly affected by the way in which their distribution runs are arranged, access and length both being important. The placing of radiators may affect their efficiency, while arranging continuous access for pipework can necessitate expensive expedients.

It is rarely, if ever, possible to arrange a building solely so as to get the best out of the services – and if it were this might entail so much compromise on the general convenience of the occupants as to be thoroughly undesirable – but the provision of short circulations and the accessibility of services without affecting the occupation of rooms should usually be among the designer's aims.

A choice may have to be made between running heating, hot and cold water and plumbing services around the perimeter of a residential block and using a spine distribution. In the first case, radiators could be placed under windows (which many prefer, though heat loss through the external envelope needs to be minimised) and lavatory basins can be given good natural light. A horizontal duct around each floor can run under windows from a vertical duct near the stair and lifts. Both vertical and horizontal ducts can have continuous access, though in the latter case the services could only be worked on from residents' rooms. Runs would be comparatively long, and the provision of adequate falls to wastes could be difficult. The alternative is to run services above a suspended ceiling over the central corridor, with short spurs serving rooms above on either side. This will shorten pipe runs, and give easy access to services without the need to enter rooms.

The advantages of each option need to be assessed quite carefully in any particular case, and there is no obvious 'best' arrangement that should be universally adopted. The contrast is rarely sufficiently striking to justify the sacrifice (say) of a good room layout. It should, however, be one of the factors taken into account in determining such a layout, and other basic decisions on the nature of the plan to be adopted.

Similar considerations will apply to the ventilation system.

The arrangement and size of ducts needs in any case to be established at a very early stage of design, as these can be a key factor. Often this means that unnecessarily large ducts are provided: even if the ducts and crawlways seem ample in size, detailed layouts to show which services are to use which parts of them have to be made if they are to be used to the best advantage.

The electrical services rarely make critical demands, though the need to provide a substation, if it arises, will be the subject of stringent control and needs early consideration.

Mechanical systems

The provision of lifts and mechanical handling systems within the building, where these are required, inevitably makes precise demands in terms of size and siting, and it may be necessary in extreme cases virtually to design the building around such an installation. Unless exact information is available, it is often necessary to overprovide space wastefully for such systems, and it may be better to delay until exact requirements are known.

Drainage

The Building Regulations ensure that our drainage systems are sound and accessible – it is the designer's responsibility to ensure that they are also simple and economical. This is achieved by siting and grouping outlets so as to shorten drain runs, minimise depths and limit the number of inspection chambers. In turn, this can profoundly affect the planning of the building.

None of the services should usually be regarded as so important that its demands take priority over all other considerations in determining the form of the building, but each must be given its due weight. It is usually a balance between the optima which will provide the most acceptable overall design.

Technology in general

It has not been possible, nor would it have been appropriate, to describe in detail here every technological condition that might influence design. Enough examples have, I trust, been given to establish a basic principle:

It is necessary for decisions on the materials and methods of construction to be adopted to be arrived at early, and to be made on logical grounds. Once such a decision has been taken, the consequences must be accepted as part of the constraints within which the design is being prepared. It is therefore essential that such decisions should be taken thoughtfully and in the light of all relevant considerations.

Site

A further set of factors which can, and should, have a considerable effect on the nature of the building are those imposed by the selected site. The site will, naturally, have been selected and evaluated for its suitability to the proposed purpose – nonetheless no site is ideal, and there will always be some variations to the design in response to site conditions. Anyone who has attempted to adapt a developed design to an alternative site knows how far-reaching such variations may be.

Position and accessibility

The sprawling building which may be right on a country site may be compared with the more compact one more likely to be designed for a town centre. This is not only a response to relative land costs, but due to our feeling of the formality that is suitable in a town, and to what is known (architecturally) as 'urbanity', and the more relaxed informality we expect to find in the country.

The availability or otherwise of public transport may affect the scope of car parking provision needed – and shielding an extensive car park so that it doesn't dominate a design can be an important consideration. Is it to be built into the basement, concealed by landscaping, or expensively taken to a remote corner?

Surroundings

The character of the surroundings of any site ought to have a profound effect on the design proposed by any responsible architect. Whether he wishes to conform to the existing character of development in the area (or is constrained to do so by the planning authority) or wishes to provide a relief in contrast to it, he can hardly help being influenced by what is there already. The heights of adjacent buildings and their density will affect the way in which his building is understood by passers-by, and so must be taken into account. So must the materials, colours and textures they present – and if they are very close he may have to take into account that windows have acquired rights of light (see Ch. 13). Though people have no right to a view, he may not wish to actually destroy a pleasant prospect for someone else. If a nice view exists, getting the best from it for the occupants of his building should be very important to him.

The existence of shops near the site, the closeness of churches, pubs and schools could affect the way he places his building (he may well want to shield occupants from the noise of the last two!). He will not want nearby industrial development to be obtrusive if he is designing an old persons' home: if he is designing a factory, he will not want it, in turn, to obtrude.

Additionally, he must be aware of the danger of building operations causing damage to existing property – and will wish to note any existing damage to nearby buildings, so that this cannot be attributed to building operations later.

Further, the orientation of the site will affect the arrangement of the accommodation to achieve the best aspects for the rooms.

Size and shape

The size and shape of the building will quite naturally and evidently respond to the shape and size of the site to be used. The fact that this might mean a slightly less convenient or more expensive building is not, however, always so well understood. A building on a city site may well have to 'fit' the site's general shape – this can mean that the amount of accommodation on each floor does not precisely conform to the amount which could be most economically served by toilets and lifts.

Additionally, the expense of developing the site will be affected by the difficulty the builder might have in providing huts and storage space and making sensible use of plant. If circulation space for building operations is limited, and if extreme measures have to be taken to protect the public, this should be taken into account when the building is designed (Fig. 5.9).

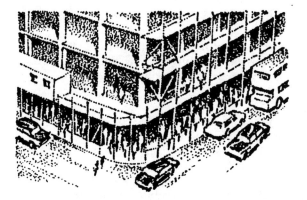

Fig. 5.9 Work in tight conditions may be impossible unless the design is modified

Levels

The site with irregular levels is often the most rewarding to develop, in terms of the interest of the eventual design. Developing it can be expensive, though, and thought has to be given to the economics of earth movement, and to the desirability of arranging blocks to follow rather than to cross the contours. The aim will usually be to enhance rather than to flatten the general levels of the site, and its three-dimensional shape will be in the forefront of the designer's mind. He will constantly need to balance exploitation of the fascinating character of the land against economics – and very often a less than optimum arrangement of rooms may be decided upon, in order that the sculptural form of the building should complement that of the site.

Trees and existing features

A healthy, full-grown tree adds far more to the enjoyment of any building than fragile new planting will be able to for many years. An early step, when there are existing trees on site, ought always to be to get them surveyed by a competent person, to determine which are best worth preserving. Once a decision to preserve is taken, this can profoundly affect both the design and the operations of the builder.

If trees are to be preserved, they need to be protected from building damage, and the building has to be protected from the trees – roots and falling leaves can make full-grown trees unpopular with people living in their immediate vicinity, although they are greatly admired as generalised elements in the environment.

There may be other features on site which should be preserved – streams, hedgerows, shrubberies, fences and small buildings may all be valuable assets (visually as well as financially) which it would be folly to destroy. Their preservation may severely limit the designer's options, however.

The initial aim will usually be to preserve and enhance all truly worthwhile features where this can sensibly be done, but not to feel a slavish need to preserve every weedy tree or boundary wall.

Conclusions

In general, the designer will regard the site as the second most important condition of his operations, after the client's requirements, and it is common to think of the design as a response to the functional brief modified by the characteristics of the site.

The site may well also be considered as a technical restraint, however, because the actual forms of construction which can be adopted will in many ways result from the demands of site conditions.

Example

In the case of the factory building, referred to in Chapter 2, the designer will clearly need to choose materials which will stand up to hard treatment while retaining their strength and appearance. He will want to choose a structure which avoids freestanding internal columns, since these might make the arrangement of machinery difficult, and it could seem desirable to opt for a construction which would facilitate later alterations if the manufacturer changed the nature of his product or the scope of his operations, or if the building changed hands.

Since in at least part of the building dust extraction and humidity control are important, early thought will need to be given to the design of the plant, and its requirements.

Deliveries and despatch are also important, and trucks will have to come on-site to the loading bay, preferably without detriment to safety or appearance.

The main constraint imposed by the site, apart from the low height of adjacent buildings, is that the stream could be an attractive feature of the neighbourhood if it could be opened up to view. This is on the south side of the site, while the road access is to the north. There are also two attractive existing trees which it would be helpful to retain.

It would be worthwhile to consider carefully before ruling out the possibility of choosing solid fuel – even if gas-fired boilers are installed initially, future changes in relative costs, and public policy, might make it wise to retain the possibility of future change.

Chapter 6

Factory production

Prefabrication systems

The processes of construction are increasingly being transferred from the variable and often unpleasant conditions of the site to the controlled environment of the factory, and this is occurring in spite of, and parallel to, the trend to up-grade site conditions to approximate more closely to those found in the workshop. It is not, of course, a particularly new tendency. We regard the special design of many elements (lavatory basins, doors, door furniture) as a luxury to be reserved for the occasional prestige building, being normally perfectly happy to select from the standard ranges offered by manufacturers. Even if doors are purpose designed, we expect they will be made by a specialist firm in factory conditions. The joiner does not set up a bench on site for the purpose.

Bricks are prefabricated units of even longer standing. The delivery of prepared components rather than raw materials to site has a respectable ancestry.

What is generally meant by 'prefabrication' goes a little further than this. Much larger components – whole wall panels complete with fittings, or even whole sections of the building, cut down into lorry sized sections – are delivered. There is usually the implication that the assembly of these units on a prepared base will be accomplished by 'dry' techniques. The need for the completion of services and finishes varies with the system.

There are two main classes of prefabricated system about. In each a particular manufacturer tends to hold a monopoly for the supply of the components, and therefore, though tenders for similar buildings in competing systems can be obtained, these are not truly competitive since every system offers different advantages. There is also some prospect of the development of interchangeable units from a variety of firms, leading to the possibility of truly competitive tendering.

Closed systems

A closed system is analogous to one of those plastic kits from which a model aircraft can be built.

All the parts are there, together with detailed instructions – but try as you will, only one satisfactory end-result can be attained. If the kit says the aircraft is a Messerschmidt, there is no way of building a Spitfire from the parts: if the manufacturer has designed a particular house type, you can't make a different one from the kit (Fig. 6.1).

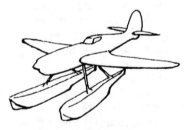

Fig. 6.1 A closed system of prefabrication can produce only one result

Some of the early postwar prefabricated houses were of this kind. Entire houses arrived on-site in sections, complete with fitted and plumbed kitchens and bathrooms, central heating and electricity, and were rapidly erected on prepared bases. These were, in fact, excellent houses, and remarkably well equipped for the period. As, though, they had been designed for only a limited life and were left in use for many further years, they became shabby and somewhat outdated, and unfortunately the term 'prefab' gained unjustified dowdy associations in the public mind. These houses also tended to give the public the idea that prefabrication inevitably meant standardisation. Such ingrained ideas have proved an unfortunate barrier to widespread acceptance of the advantages of factory production of buildings.

Production of closed-system buildings requires a large flow of orders for an identical product, so it is suitable for individual houses, holiday chalets, garages and site offices and other temporary buildings. There is no need for the parts to be interchangeable, or related to a dimensional grid, any more than this is required for assembly-line production of motor cars.

Open systems

An open system is much more flexible, and can be compared to the sets of inter-related building blocks, from which an imaginative child can build anything from a farm to a moon station (Fig. 6.2).

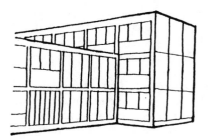

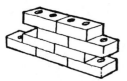

Fig. 6.2 An open system of prefabrication is capable of many permutations

The manufacturer develops a range of dimensionally compatible parts which can be assembled in many different ways to produce a wide range of buildings of varying size, function, and number of storeys. There is likely to be a variety of spans available, as well as a number of floor to floor heights and several different window, door and other cladding panels will be offered.

It is essential that the design of the joints has been so refined that the parts are virtually completely interchangeable, and (armed with the catalogue) the architect has a flexible – though limited – vocabulary with which to design. Provided he accepts the constraints of the three-dimensional planning grid, he can be free to design at will. Some designers find it hard to accept such stringent conditions, and find

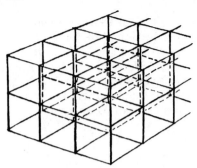

Fig. 6.3 If a single grid were adopted as standard, could parts from many manufacturers become interchangeable?

systems of this kind impossibly constraining; others have a different experience, and find freedom from the need to consider the practicality of every conjunction of parts (provided the system recognises such a possibility), the lack of need to think about flashings and foundations, stimulating to creativity.

The building can never be better than the original system, of course, and there is great responsibility laid upon the manufacturer to ensure that the individual components are sensitively designed, well proportioned and simple, and that the whole collection will produce unified and rhythmic buildings.

Catalogue systems

A major difficulty of both open and closed systems is the impossibility of meaningful competitive tendering. It is necessary first to select the contractor on some comparative basis, and then to work within his system.

One way in which we may find the industry develops may offer an escape from this dilemma. Many components already (windows and kitchen fittings for example) are interchangeable. If either (a) the design of joints for dry systems were standardised, or (b) more 'wet' assembly was considered acceptable, it would become possible to put together prefabricated buildings using components manufactured by many different firms, and to obtain competitive tenders for individual components. This is a development of the way in which many different parts of buildings are selected today, and evolution along these lines seems highly desirable (Fig. 6.3).

Advantages

Some of the anticipated advantages of factory production have proved to be largely illusory, but it is worth considering the following points.

Speed

Certainly, site erection of the factory-made building is very speedy indeed. However, it is usually found that the time from initiation of the project to occupation is little different in the case of a building which uses an open system of prefabrication and in the case of one of conventional construction. Planning is as lengthy a business, and though no superstructure details have to be prepared, there is still a full set of documents needed for the substructure, services, finishes and site works, as well as arrangement drawings for the superstructure, so the time saved at this point is slight. Once the order is placed, the components practically always have to be specially manufactured. It is rare for a manufacturer to hold stocks of any but the most basic parts, and no programme, so far as I am aware, has yet succeeded in providing anything like the continuous production runs normal in the motor car industry. The order may have to wait its turn, and then the shop will be jigged-up to provide the parts for this particular building. The work, once started, will normally be continuous, rapid, and unaffected by the weather.

Once a delivery date is known, the general contractor can programme his site work to have a prepared slab ready when deliveries of components start, so there can be a little telescoping of the programme. The superstructure is, of course, very rapidly erected, but finishes, services and site works commonly are completed in the conventional manner, and take just as long as they would for any other job.

Cost

It was hoped, during the euphoric early days of prefabrication as a widespread technique, that factory production would mean efficiency and efficiency would lead to economy. These hopes have by no means been fully realised.

Although a joiner working in his own shop can produce reasonably priced one-off kitchen fittings, no one would expect to produce one-off windows or pressed-steel lintols as cheaply as can be done in a factory run. Where windows have been specially designed so that they can be assembled by semi-skilled labour, a factory can produce them very cheaply.

The difficulty with whole buildings is that, except for very simple repetitive units like greenhouses, the long runs which make such techniques applicable simply do not exist, though no doubt it is within the bounds of possibility that they may do so in the future. The variations between components demand the application of higher skills by the operatives, and the work is slowed down by the variety. Rejigging between jobs takes time, too, and time is costly.

There is, too, the cost of transport to be considered. To transport completed components, taking proper care of them·is considerably less economical than to transport materials in the raw state from place to place.

In general, therefore, the cost of prefabricated buildings is no cheaper than that of conventional ones, except in the case of very repetitive units like garages and huts. This situation may change.

Quality

It is in the realm of quality that prefabrication should score. People working in controlled conditions in a factory should be expected to perform nearer to their optimum for a higher proportion of their working day than workmen subjected to climatic changes and the difficult working positions so often found on the building site.

Supervision, too, can be more adequate in the shop. The work is in clear view, and can be examined freely.

The individual craftsman often claims that it is the variety of jobs and conditions which lead him to choose his craft, and that he would be unhappy in factory conditions: that the supply of craftsmen would die out if all skilled work were removed from site. Facts seem to be ahead – the supply of craftsmen is drying up in any case, and this may accelerate the move to the factory, where semi-skilled but carefully supervised workers can be employed.

Dimensional constraints

The dimensional discipline imposed on designers by prefabrication can actually be very salutary, and stimulate thought. A designer who might weakly decide to change a bay size or split a span if it were in his power, finds he cannot do so. He makes an additional effort to solve the extra problem, and produces a better building in the end, because he has accepted the constraints of the construction, and his building is a refined statement of those constraints. Buildings which abide by imposed rules, do in fact tend to turn out better than undisciplined ones, anyway. Constraints seem to be a necessary condition for good design.

In the design of the system itself, a three-dimensional grid giving overall horizontal and vertical limitations should have been established, on the lines shown in Fig. 6.3. This will control the increments at which structures can be planned. This will not mean, however, that the components will precisely fit the nominal sizes stated. Allowance has to be made for plus and minus manufacturing tolerances (which will depend on the materials and method of manufacture) for inaccuracies in setting out, and for the physical difficulty of fitting an object into a matching space (site tolerances) and for thermal movement (expansion gap). Fig. 6.4 shows this diagrammatically and it can be seen that every component will have a nominal size and a

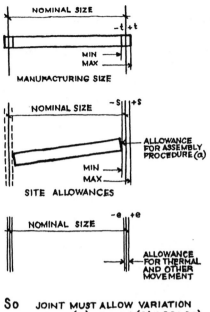

SO JOINT MUST ALLOW VARIATION
FROM 'a' TO a+(2t+2s+2e)

Fig. 6.4 With dry construction, the design of joints becomes critical.

manufacturing size, neither of which is likely to be its actual size. The difference has to be taken up in the design of the joints, which are crucial to the success of any system.

Design of joints and fixings

If prefabricated buildings are to be assembled dry, the design of joints is critical, and it is frequently by the performance of the joints that such systems stand or fall. They have to be devised to react to a number of different conditions satisfactorily:

1. They must be tough enough to withstand the actual assembly process without damage or distortion. A joint may appear excellent on paper, but if it is hard to assemble without a gasket being doubled back it will not be acceptable on site.
2. They must be secure and self-supporting during assembly.
3. They must respond satisfactorily to all the dimensional variations which arise from the situations discussed in the last section.
4. They must be fully weathertight, including the intersections between joints. Frequently they are designed to act as internal gutters, allowing the water to penetrate part way and then channelling it out of the building.

5. The weights of the components must be properly supported through extremes of weather. A fail-safe device ought to be incorporated so that if one fixing fails the load will still be carried until a repair is carried out.

Chapter 7

Aesthetics

Vocabulary of aesthetics

Aesthetics is a branch of philosophy – like all sciences. Like other sciences it is concerned with discovery and with explanation of widely observed phenomena. The area it explores is that of the experience we call 'beauty', and the emotions aroused by it, which it seeks to observe, define and explain.

A great many of us can recognise a satisfactory design – a beautiful object – practically on sight, yet would be hard put to it to point to the particular features which contribute to its success. Even more, they find creating a good design a very hit-and-miss affair. Experience in design leads us all to at least some notion of which devices and ways of putting things together are most likely to 'work', because we all learn from experience. We don't expect to struggle with mathematics or chemistry, though, on a trial-and-error basis, and neither should we where aesthetics are concerned. In precisely the same way that mathematics has developed – through observation, the proposition and testing of hypotheses to the establishment of working 'rules' – so aesthetics has evolved through the experience of generations a formulated and generally accepted theory.

We may 'know what we like' – but we can also understand why we like it. A designer should be able to produce a design he knows will be acceptable (and that he will 'like') by applying accepted theories he understands. Indeed we should regard 'correctness' as a better criterion of success than 'liking'. An objective judgement should be preferred to a subjective one.

What is familiar may be accepted uncritically, while what is strange demands an intellectual effort of understanding. It is therefore easier to like something which has echoes of the past than to follow designers down new paths. This does not, however, invalidate what seems at first sight odd and alien. Understanding of the rules of aesthetics will allow even the most innovative designs to be properly evaluated.

This chapter aims to set out the principal rules of visual aesthetics as they affect buildings, though examples from other fields of design will be referred to to explain the rules.

Unity

Unity need not imply monotony or meaningless repetition. It is, though, a characteristic of good design that all the parts should be clearly seen as contributing towards a single whole, and this entails a certain family likeness between the constituents. This may be true of a whole town (Bath, Harlow) of a street, of a single building or of the furnishing and accessories of a building. The sense of unity gives a sensation of completeness which is anything but dull. It does not even demand absence of conflict, only that the dynamic forces generated by the features of the design are held in balance and resolved within its boundaries.

A number of factors will contribute towards this sense of wholeness. For every aspect of every feature to be slavishly repeated would of course be monotonous in the extreme, and it is a matter of the judicious application of a highly developed aesthetic awareness to determine the extent of variation within the overall framework that is desirable. In general, I would suggest, there should be a strong degree of unity in at least three of the fields described below, which will serve to enhance the variations admitted to other elements of the composition.

Unity of colour

Colour theory is discussed later in this chapter. At this point it is only necessary to emphasise the desirability of a strong colour policy running through a design. The selection of a limited range of colours and materials can allow scope for considerable variation in the ways in which they are combined and employed, while helping to draw together the various elements of the design. Commercial firms are well aware of this, and study of the 'housestyle' of any great manufacturer will show that the repetitive use of carefully selected colours is a very important feature in our recognition of their product and promotional material. We may even go so far as to learn from such firms that the use of a single dominant colour can unify even very diverse object.

From different fields, the famous black and white 'Ascot' scene from the film *My Fair Lady* (Osbert Lancaster) and the unity imposed on the city of Bath by the use over generations of the local stone exemplify this principle.

Texture

Texture, if it is to be appreciated visually rather than by tactile means, is virtually a further aspect of colour, related to value, (see 'Munsell', p. 137). In addition, however, it has an important effect on the character of a design and if randomly chosen textures are used together uncomfortable conflicts can be caused. This may be most readily understood in costume, where the textures of denim and cheesecloth, or velvet and brocade, might give acceptable combinations, but the use of denim with brocade or cheesecloth with velvet would take a good deal of care in ensuring sufficient unity of colour, proportion, line, motif and so on to make it acceptable. In building, highly finished marble with rough random stonework, or stained, adzed timber with mosaic might give rise to clashes that were difficult to resolve.

Conversely, by considering textural similarities, sometimes family relationships can be revealed among otherwise incompatible elements. By emphasising ruggedness as a characteristic of concrete, and timber, and landscape, a composition might be unified that would be unacceptable if the concrete was clad in mosaic, the timber was stained, and the landscape a matter of lawns and flowering cherries – excellent though each of those elements might be in a different context.

Unity of shape

The reasons for the adoption of the pointed arch in gothic churches were undoubtedly those of engineering rather than those of aesthetics (see Ch. 5). It is equally true, however, that the repetition of this form has a powerful unifying effect on the aesthetics of the design. The reasons for the choice of form hardly matter in this context – the repetition itself is the essential feature. A particular angle adopted for oblique lines, a consistent use of circles or hexagons, or the choice of a square or other regular planning grid will have a similar effect.

There are good reasons for not making arbitrary choices in this area as any other. I know of one building where insistence on the adoption of an unusually shaped planning grid for the sake of creating an unusual (though undoubtedly unified) building, has caused very considerable difficulties in planning and in construction and has very much increased the cost of the whole project. In this case it is hard to discern a logical basis for the choice, and the whole looks contrived. It will usually be more satisfactory if the needs of the plan, or of the construction, or of some other vital aspect of the design are evidently the underlying genesis of the selection of the shape.

There are occasions when one very important element of a design suggests a shape which is so dominant that it becomes a 'signature' of the whole, and is used in a purely decorative way. This can be an excellent reason for the choice of a decorative motif. At the Crucible Theatre in Sheffield (architects: Renton Howard Wood Levin Partnership) this has been done very successfully. The octagon shape generated on a purely theatrical and functional basis for the plan of the auditorium has been adopted as a keynote motif, and is even used to identify promotional material (Fig. 7.1).

See also the notes on 'applied decoration' later in this chapter.

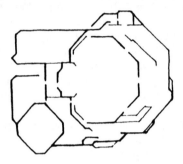

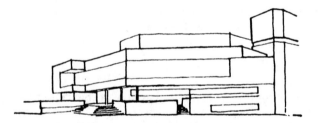

Fig. 7.1 The octagon adopted in the Crucible Theatre for functional reasons becomes the main design motif

Unity of scale

For the great majority of buildings, human scale will provide a reference point by which the size of all the elements will be judged. Doorways, steps, table tops all have to be designed to be used, and the sizes will be determined by their use (see Ch. 4).

If some elements are abnormally large or unnaturally small we are conscious of oddity and discomfort. There is charm in a consistent miniature, as we all discover when we visit one of the model villages which are such an attraction to tourists, and overscale gives a sense of grandeur, as visitors to St Peter's' Rome' will testify. In each of these cases. a single feeling for scale runs through the whole, and this must be the case if the design is to be successful. Special small doors for the keepers in an elephant house, or one teacher-sized desk in a primary classroom can look incongruous (Fig. 7.2).

Establishing an appropriate scale and then applying it consistently is an important step in producing an effective design, and exerts a powerful unifying force.

Fig. 7.2 Unity of scale can easily be destroyed by one oversized element

Unity of dynamic

Rhythm and dynamics are discussed later (pp. 127, 132). Suffice it to mention at this point that any combination of elements creates directional forces, whose resolution is essential to the unity of the design.

Selection from commercial designs

The design work of an architect includes a surprisingly large element of the selection from designs actually produced by other people of components suitable for his purpose. For example, it would only be for the largest or most prestigious buildings that door furniture or sanitaryware would be specially designed: standard doors and windows are commonly selected: there is a discernible tendency for more and more (and larger) mass-produced items to be assembled to create the total effect.

Where such components have been designed by a variety of different minds, acting under motivations which can only be guessed at (but may reasonably be expected to have manufacturing and economic considerations high in the order of priorities) the responsibility of the designer to produce a unified whole can be an especially difficult one to discharge. The need to establish strong and unifying characteristics becomes particularly vital.

This might be done by severe limitation of colour, or of material, or of proportion, or by setting a strong three-dimensional design grid to which all the major features of the design must conform. For example, a strong line at window cill height, carried round in worktops, shelves and other features, and another at door head height used for transoms and the tops of cupboards could do much to discipline an assembly of diverse elements (see also Ch. 6 and Fig. 7.3).

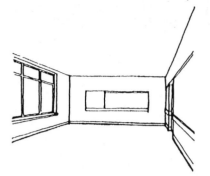

Fig. 7.3 The discipline imposed by limitations on dimensional increments enhances the unity of a design

Proportion

What IS 'good proportion'?

Even the term is frequently misunderstood, which is hardly surprising, since it means a number of different things. The term can refer to at least three aspects of the same design.

Taking the very simple example of a coffee mug decorated with a single coloured band. We might be concerned with the relationship of the width to the height of the mug, with the relationship between the size of the handle and the body of the mug, or with the width and placing of the band. All these are aspects of good proportion, and for the mug to be 'well proportioned' all three relationships would have to be satisfactory (Fig. 7.4).

Fig. 7.4 The width to height ratio, the handle to body relationship and the size and placing of the band are all aspects of the good proportions of this mug

The same is true of the design of a building. When a Georgian façade is spoken of as 'well proportioned', the relationship between the height and breadth of the elevation, the relationship between height and width of each opening, and the relationship between those dimensions and the distances between them, as well as the overall ratio of opening to solid wall are considered satisfactory. If one were considering a building 'in the round', rather than a façade, a further dimension (of depth) and a further relationship (between volumes) would enter the reckoning (Fig. 7.5).

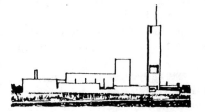

Fig. 7.5 The proportions of window to wall, of height to length and of one volume to another are aspects of the good proportions of this building

As design proceeds, smaller and smaller details need to be considered, but always the proportions of the item itself, its relationship to the whole, and its placing, have to be considered. All must be satisfactorily arranged.

All of these aspects of proportion are governed by the same rules. Certain attractive relationships have been identified over the years, and of these probably the 'golden section' is the most important and well known (Fig. 7.6). At times it is fashionable to use particular

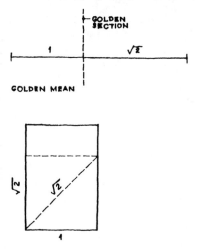

Fig. 7.6 The golden section

proportions – the square or an attenuated 2:5 will each impose a particular character on a design that might look trendy at the time, but rapidly look dated as newer proportions come into fashion. It can, in general, be said that extreme proportions are rarely entirely satisfactory, and that part of being 'well proportioned' consists in avoiding extremes of any kind.

Proportions of 2:3 (Fig. 7.7) and 3:5 (Fig. 7.8) may be easier to apply than the golden section, while less banal than 3:4 (Fig. 7.9). The illustrations show the effect of each of the systems mentioned applied to linear, plan and spatial arrangements.

It should be noted that (as is the case of all aspects of aesthetics) consistency is important. If one proportion cannot be adhered to in all aspects of the design, related systems (2:3:5, 2:3, 3:5, 2:5) can perhaps be applied.

The shape of A-series paper is interesting because the proportion between the sides is such (1:1.414) that every time the paper is folded along its long side the proportions remain the same.

Classical Greek buildings are particularly valued for the fine proportioning of all the parts, both within themselves and in relation to the whole (Fig. 7.10). Much effort has been put into analysing the geometric basis of these (and later) loved and admired buildings, and it can generally be seen that order and care in placing the larger and the detailed parts makes a logical framework for the whole design.

The subtleties of building design demand great skill in handling the very complex elements concerned in a consistently well proportioned manner.

![2:3 linear diagram]

2 : 3

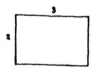

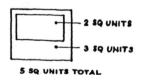

2 SQ UNITS
3 SQ UNITS
5 SQ UNITS TOTAL

Fig. 7.7 The 2:3 relationship

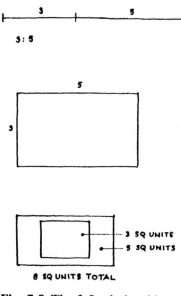

Fig. 7.8 The 3:5 relationship

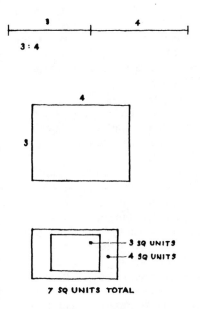

Fig. 7.9 The 3:4 relationship tends to be banal

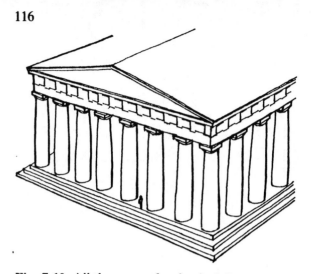

Fig. 7.10 All the parts of a classical Greek building are carefully related to one another

Balance

One essential characteristic of a unified design is that it has a focal point: there is some particular spot on which the eye will naturally rest. It is, of course, of some importance that this point should be identified and the balance of the whole design and all its elements arranged around it carefully so that the focal point is unambiguous. This careful handling will provide a design structure that is easily read and understood, no matter how much of design interest and detail there may be for the observer to explore at his leisure.

If there is a particular aspect of the design to which the designer wishes attention to be drawn (the face in a costume design, perhaps, or the switches of a radio) he will be wise to arrange matters so that the natural focal point coincides with that of his design. If fulcrum and importance do not coincide, conflict will result.

In the design of a poster, one could arrange for the date of a disco, the venue, the group, or the cost, to occupy the focal point, at will – depending on which was thought likely to be most attractive to the potential audience (Fig. 7.11). Where a building is in question, it is quite common to arrange the balance to emphasise the main entrance. If this lies at the design focus, it may be most readily found by strangers. Alternatively, in the case of a large building with one overridingly important element of accommodation it may be thought appropriate to attribute all importance to that space. So the chancel of a church, or the proscenium of a theatre, may reasonably occupy the focal position (Fig. 7.12).

Obtaining the kind of visual balance around this point, that is being referred to here, is very similar in principle to obtaining a

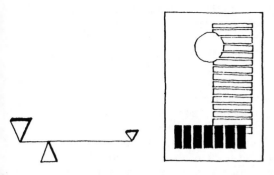

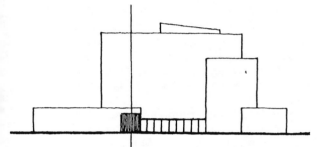

Fig. 7.11 Visual and physical balance work in similar ways

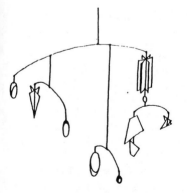

Fig. 7.12 It is important that the fulcrum of the design is at a suitable point for the eye to rest

Fig. 7.13 The delicate balance of a mobile is sir·ilar to the subtlety of many building designs

physical balance of weights on a balance arm, or in a suspended 'mobile' (Fig. 7.13). Exactly as the weight of such physical objects may be unrelated to their bulk, and a small steel ball may outweigh a mass of wood shavings, for example, so it is not only size that will determine the visual 'weight' of an item in a composition. The interest, detail, colour, shape, and every other aspect will count, and in particular one item which contrasts from any point of view with its surroundings will gain additional 'weight'.

Symmetry

A symmetrical balance is one in which each element in the design is exactly reflected on the other side of a central focus. Notice that the presence of a central focal point is not in itself sufficient to produce symmetry – the balancing items must be identical and identically placed. Very subtle effects can be achieved by including some balancing but non-identical groups of elements in what purports to be a symmetrical design, but this should strictly be considered an occult balance.

A kilogramme of lead and a kilogramme of feathers arranged equidistant from a fulcrum, would maintain a beam in balance (Fig. 7.14) but this would not produce symmetry. The same is true visually (Fig. 7.15). Equally, two kilogrammes of lead, one on each side of the fulcrum, will only maintain the balance of the beam if they are placed equidistant from the fulcrum – this, too, has a parallel in the visual realm (Fig. 7.16).

In symmetry, every addition or alteration made to one side of the composition must be answered by a corresponding alteration or addition on the other. It is not necessary, however, for each or any of these parts to be symmetrical in itself, though there may be cases where considerations of unity lead to this being wished for. However, it is often helpful if the designs of the parts tend to lead the eye a little towards the central focus.

Duality

There is, indeed, some danger of producing competing centres of interest if one symmetrical composition is balanced by another (Fig. 7.17). This case illustrates what is meant by the term 'duality' and a situation to be avoided: remember the donkey who died of starvation halfway between two equal bunches of carrots! The eye which does not know on which of two conflicting foci to rest will be tired and confused: the design will certainly be neither satisfactory nor enjoyed.

The resolution of a duality can be achieved in two ways. Firstly, an overriding, central, focus can be imposed, sufficiently strong to master the divisive forces (Fig. 7.18). The effect of this can be enhanced if the detail design of the components is subtly changed to show some deference to the central focus (Fig. 7.19). By doing this, a single, symmetrical composition can be produced.

Alternatively, the parts can be so altered that a total composition in assymetrical balance is produced, because one of the competing foci

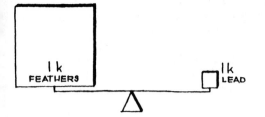

Fig. 7.14 Lead can balance feathers – but that isn't symmetry

Fig. 7.15 Symmetry isn't just a matter of having a central focal point

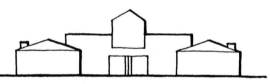

Fig. 7.16 In symmetry, like balances like

Fig. 7.17 Duality

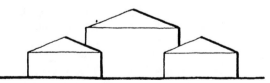

Fig. 7.18 The duality is resolved

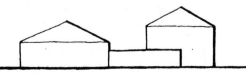

Fig. 7.19 The duality is removed by moving the focus

has clearly become dominant. It will not be enough simply to make the parts different from one another – the whole must be considered as an occult balance (see Fig. 7.20). Notice that in this case the focal point of the entire composition will not lie on the visual centre of gravity of the dominant element, and will need to be recognised and marked. Exactly as in the case of a 4 kg and a 1 kg weight in equilibrium on a beam, the centre of gravity lies proportionately between the two (Fig. 7.21).

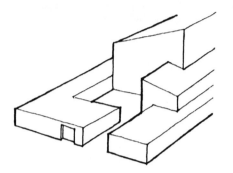

Fig. 7.20 Occult balance

Fig. 7.21 Like balances unlike

Occult (assymetrical) balance

By resolving a duality as described, what is known as 'occult' or assymmetrical, balance is produced. This is something which is often the deliberate aim of a designer from the outset.

The visual weight of each element is carefully considered, and the placing of each element in relation to the whole is carefully done in the light of the effect it will have on the overall equilibrium of the design.

If this is understood in the analogy of the balance of forces on a beam cantilevered on either side of a single support (Fig. 7.22) and then the subtle balance of the elements of a suspended mobile is considered (Fig. 7.23) the great delicacy needed to produce a well balanced occult design in three dimensions will be appreciated. It will be seen, too, how easily apparently unimportant minor alterations to a design can destroy such careful balance.

On the whole, symmetrical designs tend to be more formal in their effect, and suitable to public buildings and cases where an imposing or solemn mood is desired, while occult designs are less formal, and suit domestic and leisure buildings.

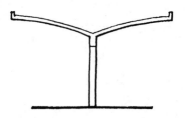

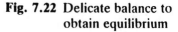

Fig. 7.22 Delicate balance to obtain equilibrium

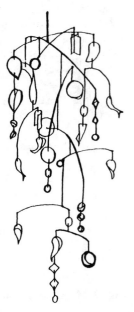

Fig. 7.23 Balance can be elaborated with great subtlety

Classical and articulated compositions

Formality is also an attribute of the 'classical' type of design in which an outer envelope encloses within a single form all the intricacies of the object. A less formal kind of design 'articulates' the elements from which the object is made up, so that the mechanism can easily be read. Most modern kitchen fittings are designed in the classical way, so that there is little external difference between a cooker, a washing machine or a refrigerator. A generation or so ago, a cooker could clearly be seen to consist of grill, oven and hotplate, and the early washing machines obviously had a tub and a wringer (Fig. 7.24).

Buildings can be designed in either way, and it can almost seem, at times, to be an arbitrary choice which form is adopted, and a matter more of fashion than of expression of the nature of the building.

Compare the Parthenon with Salisbury cathedral, or Compton Wynyates with Queen's House (Fig. 7.25).

A 'classical' design, in building, is not (as is sometimes supposed) a matter of the adoption of a particular vocabulary of decorative detail. It has much more to do with a feeling for formality and oneness, and in many classical designs obtaining a dignified and unified exterior appearance has been given priority over other design considerations. Articulated (sometimes thought of as 'romantic') designs, on the other hand, tend to give priority to the organisation of the interior of the building, expressing this as the principal

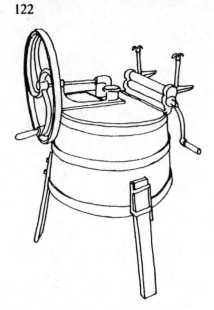

Fig. 7.24 An articulated design

COMPTON WYNYATES

QUEEN'S HOUSE

Fig. 7.25 Articulated and classical compositions

characteristic of the external appearance. A good classical design will not have sacrificed convenience in use entirely to looks, though, and neither will a romantic one have sacrificed appearance entirely to function. As has previously been emphasised (Ch. 2) the integration of the demands of appearance, function and technology to obtain a totally satisfactory design solution from all points of view is the hallmark of architecture as opposed to mere building. The order in which these aspects are approached will influence the total character of the design (Fig. 7.26).

Fig. 7.26 Good design comes from the interaction of all the requirements

Character

The character, or individual personality, of a building (or any other artefact) emerges from the fruitful interaction of all the factors of aesthetics, as they relate to use and construction. Character seems to have a great deal to do with the aesthetic sensibility of the designer, present but unconscious as he considers the other influences of the design.

Character has a number of components, some of which are considered below.

The term '*massing*' is applied to architectural design, with the implication that the design must have equal validity no matter from what aspect it is observed. This would be true of sculpture, but not (for example) for a stage set on a proscenium stage, or a shop window display. Getting the massing right is one of the earliest tasks of design – if it is satisfactory the details will fall into place happily, while if it is wrong no amount of attention to detail will correct it (Fig. 7.27).

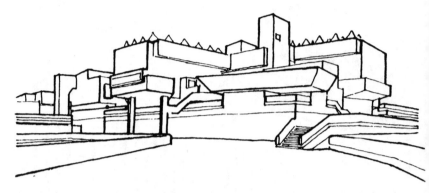

Fig. 7.27 The characteristics of the main features are strong enough to be unaffected by the decorative detail

Style is an attribute of all good design, contributing vitally to character, yet the word is widely misunderstood, because of its very ambiguity. Analogy from the world of fashion may make this clear. A man may (for the theatre) dress in Georgian style: to identify with his peers he may adopt punk style. A man however, who POSSESSES style will choose and wear his clothes 'stylishly' no matter what set of conventions he chooses to follow. He will have the assurance to make sensible choices within (and compatible with) the conventional framework he has chosen. What is essential is that framework should have been chosen for good reasons and not arbitrarily, and that the wearer should express his own personality through the 'style' selected (Fig. 7.28).

Fig. 7.28 Style and stylishness are not the same thing

The same is true of architecture. Here, too, fancy dress may sometimes seem desirable. The Germans rebuilding Nürnberg tried to follow its old form as far as possible, whereas at Coventry in similar circumstances the British chose what they felt was an 'honest' modern idiom. Both produced acceptable, living towns for the twentieth century. The replacement of one bomb-damaged house in a Georgian terrace in Bath conformed to its neighbours. It was 'fancy dress' to avoid the destruction of a total, valuable, picture.

It may seem desirable to adopt a style somehow considered 'suitable' for a building type – a church, say, or an entertainment complex. The deliberate adoption of any style (if that is interpreted as meaning a set of decorative or structural devices) is a dangerous decision. To decide that a sense of peace, or liveliness, or sophistication, however, is appropriate, is safer. Architecture results from a balance between many constraints, which may often conflict and can rarely fully be consciously considered. In the same way that the stylish man will (it may appear instinctively) put on the 'right' clothes, and be stylishly clad, so the architect will see the character of his building emerge without reference to particular idioms or contemporary tricks. Neither style nor character can be imposed upon a design: they must emerge from within it.

Excellence in design is timeless even though the design was produced as a response to conditions only occurring at a particular time. Fashionable design dated rapidly.

Taste is another ambiguous word. Good taste, like good manners, should go unnoticed: it is bad taste, like vulgarity, which draws attention to itself. Yet discrimination and a cultivated eye can allow choice between alternatives that is impossible to the untrained observer, and this discrimination, too, is called taste. This is discrimination in which mere knowledge of fashion has little or no part.

The connoisseur of wine can identify a good or a poor vintage – the rest of us may only somehow recognise when we are in the privileged presence of a great one.

So it is with painting, with design – and with architecture. As in the case of wine, the connoisseur of painting or architecture has had to train and practice his natural abilities, so the man who really understands architecture has done more than learn the grammar of construction. He has observed, and analysed, compared and evaluated and he has developed a depth of knowledge and confidence that can be trusted.

There is a tendency in us all to like what is familiar. The familiar is undemanding, while something strange gives us a sense of insecurity and makes us work to understand it. Putting this phenomenon together with the nostalgic charm of Cotswold villages or Norfolk flint creates powerful inertia and discourages innovation. What is new, in aesthetics as in other fields, often shocks. It may, indeed, be the deliberate aim of the designer to shock, or at any rate to startle the onlooker into careful examination of his work (Fig. 7.29).

Fig. 7.29 It may be a deliberate aim to astound!

Unless, however, there are genuine reasons to the contrary (infill in an old and valued environment excusing pastiche of the past; a challenging new functional need reflected in a demanding new building form) neither nostalgia nor shock value really have any place in the designer's vocabulary.

Fig. 7.30 The total effect is due, here, to the refusal of the architects to do other than fulfil their brief in every respect

At the Halifax Building Society headquarters (architects: Building Design Partnership) the total effect achieved results from the constraints of the brief interpreted in an uninhibited fashion by the architect, and indeed by all members of an unusually cohesive design team. The striking (indeed, some might feel, initially shocking) impact of the building is one of confidence, unity and simplicity which is ultimately almost entirely satisfying (Fig. 7.30). This could hardly have been the case if a less open-minded approach had been adopted.

Rhythm

An interplay of rhythm can have an important influence on the character of a design. The sequences of repetitive structural elements, windows and decorative features are bound to strike an observer, and the order and sophistication with which they are handled has a great influence on the success or failure of the whole effect.

The overriding rhythms usually emerge from the choice of structure, dimensional control and planning grid, but alert control of these factors is necessary if the rhythm is to be properly disciplined and not simply a powerful distraction (Fig. 7.31).

The rhythmic pattern will rarely be just a matter of applied decoration, yet simply to allow the plan and construction to speak for themselves would result in a crude, unmodulated effect. What is essential is that the choice of structural and planning grids, and of other major repetitive elements, is made in the consciousness of the rhythmic forces these will generate.

Fig. 7.31 Rhythm gives interest and unity to the facade

Within a major rhythm related to the structural bay, many buildings will be broken down into smaller parts – perhaps by cladding panels or by glazing bars. These elements will create subsidiary rhythms, whose 'beat' needs to be related to the overall structure but which can (as would be the case in music) include syncopations and subsidiary trills to catch the interest and enhance the intellectual depth of the design (Fig. 7.32).

The ways in which curving lines relate to one another, the changing relationships generated by a moving viewpoint, and the presence of occupants in a building, all need to be considered when establishing the complex counterpoint of its design.

Fig. 7.32 The intricate rhythm is here well contained within a simple basic form

Punctuation

Punctuation and emphasis are essential to the clear statement of a rhythmic pattern – but they are subsidiary features and cannot save an otherwise crude design.

Applied decoration

There is, of course, a place for applied decoration in design, so long as this is seen as a way of emphasising the excellence of·a well balanced whole, and not as a distraction from a less successful one. Decoration

Fig. 7.33 Decoration should be less important than the structural features of the design

Fig. 7.34 The emphasis made by decoration should be at existing points of interest in the composition

can enhance the good features of a concept and add to the interest and pleasure of the user.

Keeping such decoration in proportion, so that the whole object does not become a mere vehicle for the decoration, is almost always vital (Fig. 7.33). Certain rules have become accepted over the years which provide a useful groundwork within which this can be achieved.

1. The decoration should be placed at existing points of emphasis in the design, and not used to create new ones (Fig. 7.34).
2. The motifs and rhythms selected for the decoration should be related to the characteristics of the whole object.
3. The decoration should be a straightforward use of materials which might have been chosen for the part, even if it was to be undecorated. Nothing of function or construction should be sacrificed to decoration.

Repeating patterns

Repetition can often enhance the effect of decoration, and lead to a rich and satisfying result obtained quite simply.

The choice of repeat grid will usually be a key to success. Square, rectangular, dropped, hexagonal or shell grids – whichever form is chosen for a band or all-over pattern, and the size chosen, will influence the rhythmic effect and scale of the result. These grid lines will not usually be part of the finished pattern. They exist to establish the limits of repeats and will eventually be erased.

In designing any surface pattern it will be essential to work over at least six adjacent repeats, so that the rhythms and directional forces generated over the surface are evident and can be controlled. Each mark which is made upon the grid, while building up the pattern, must be repeated in precisely the same position in every unit of the grid. The shapes and colours within each unit must be identical: if any counterchange of colour or mirroring of the forms (for example) was intended, this would mean that effectively a larger grid had been adopted, superimposed upon the original one. There is no reason why this should not be done, so long as it is done consciously, the implications of scale are recognised, and at least six of the new, larger units are built up together (Fig. 7.35).

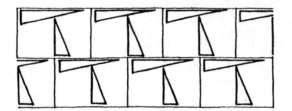

Fig. 7.35 Repetition generates it's own rhythms

Besides repeating patterns built up of free forms placed on a design grid, there are others made up of small standard units in various colours of textures. The stitches of a fairisle knitting pattern or the tiles of a floor can be used in this way. This kind of pattern can be particularly satisfying on buildings, as the discipline of the standard units exercises a powerful unifying force.

All decorative features must in themselves adhere to the rules of good design, of course. They must be carried out in suitable materials, and in a fashion that brings out the characteristics of those materials and the methods of construction, rather than trying to disguise them. It is unusual for naturalistic representations of animal or plant forms to be successful: the formalisation imposed by the limitations of techniques and materials will impose constraints upon 'lifelike' reproductions.

Works of art

Buildings make wonderful settings for sculptures and murals which are works of art in their own right (Fig. 7.36). In this case, care has to be taken that the artists chosen are sympathetic to the aims of the architect – and it has to be clear from the start whether the art is to enhance the architecture, or the reverse. The artist must be, in any event, commissioned sufficiently early to be an effective member of the design team. The visual weight, scale and dynamic of the work should be a matter for agreement between artist and architect.

Fig. 7.36 Building and sculpture enhance one another

Dynamic forces

However stationary they may be (and we hope all buildings are!) all designs create visual forces which lead the eye in one direction or another. It may be a powerful upward thrust, a floating sensation or a sense of heaviness so great that the design appears to sink. All may be appropriate in particular circumstances, and a designer has to be conscious of the dynamic of his work if he is to create the effect he wishes. A memorial chapel may be made to sit squatly on the ground, by giving it a heavy podium and carefully balanced horizontal and vertical forms, perhaps topped by a downward pressing dome (Fig. 7.37). An air terminal may reflect flight, by being set on recessed

Fig. 7.37 Weight

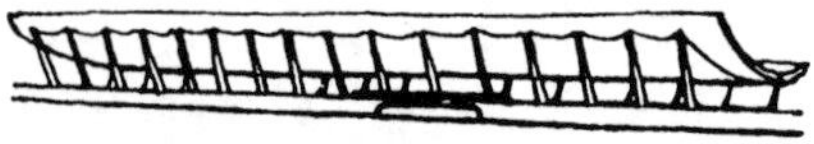

Fig. 7.38 Weightlessness

pilotis and tapered gently upwards (Fig. 7.38). Some buildings have a strong horizontal effect, often caused by repeated horizontal bands, or elongated proportions, while others are vertical in feeling (Fig. 7.39). The lines, or proportions, colours and materials can all affect the result, and the phenomena are easier to recognise then predict.

Where such strong forces are left unresolved, a very uncomfortable result can be caused. It is necessary to do two things.

1. The movement must be 'punctuated' or stopped, at its extremity. This is done by the cap of a column, for example, or by a wider blank area at the end of a row of windows (Fig. 7.40).
2. Where several directional or dynamic forces are used together, they must so be resolved (or balanced against one another) that the visual centre of gravity and the resultant of these balanced forces coincides. The apparent forces must be held in equilibrium within the composition (Fig. 7.41).

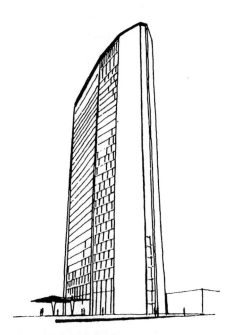

Fig. 7.39 Verticality

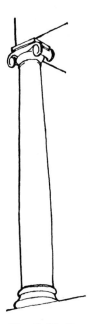

Fig. 7.40 Punctuation

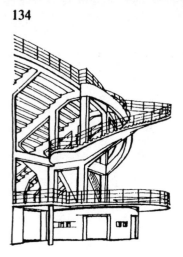

Fig. 7.41 Dynamic visual forces held in equilibrium

If a poster design is being considered, this may all seem reasonably obvious: the existence of the dynamic within the design, even an equilibrium of tensions and compressions, can lift and give excitement to the whole (Fig. 7.42). The design of a teapot is subtler. We want a

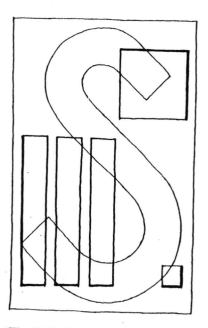

Fig. 7.42 Equilibrium in a two-dimensional design

design that appears to sit safely on its base, that looks as though it will pour efficiently (as well a doing so in fact), and that looks balanced in the hand (and actually is). This is a simple three-dimensional object. The problems with a building are similar in kind, but naturally much more complex.

After determining the overall massing to ;e achieved, a very early design decision is likely to concern the dynamic qualities of a building design.

Colour

We are all familiar from childhood paintboxes with the notion that there are three 'primary' colours which cannot be mixed from other hues – blue, red and yellow – and that given those three colours and black and white, any colour we may need can be mixed. The primaries are as intense as pigments can produce.

By mixing any two of the primaries together, a secondary colour can be obtained, and the six – three primaries and the secondaries purple, orange and green – can be arranged equidistant around the perimeter of a circle. Tertiary colours can also be achieved, again by mixing equal quantitied of adjacent colours. These twelve make up the colour wheel (Fig. 7.43).

In theory, if any colour in the wheel is mixed with the colour opposite to it (its complement) a completely neutral grey will be made. (Note that these two colours are not to be mixed in equal quantities. The idea is to obtain a perfect balance of the three primaries, which are assumed to give neutrality, so if green and red are mixed together, twice as much green as red is needed.)

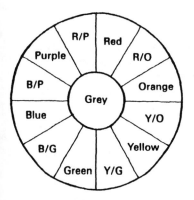

Fig. 7.43 The colour wheel

The colour obtained by mixing a little of the complement with it is known as a 'broken' (or greyed) colour. That obtained by mixing-in white is a tint, and that resulting from an addition of black is a shade. It is possible, of course, to have a shade or tint of a broken colour.

Colours that lie close together on the circle form a harmony, while those from the opposite side are contrasts.

If a colour scheme consists largely of intense colours, with one tint or shade, that constitutes a discord – often a very effective part of a colour scheme – and the same would be true of one shade among tints, for example.

This is only one of the possible approaches to colour: that of the worker with pigments. The chemist, the physiologist and the physicist each has his own point of view, and the approach of the designer to the use of colour has to take some account of each. The way the eye receives and reacts to colour images may be important if unwanted after-images are to be avoided, the way the brain responds to a colour stimulus may be vital to the creation of mood, the wavelengths of light and the ways in which it is transmitted and recorded may be significant, and the chemical reaction of one material on another could have a disastrous effect on an otherwise well considered scheme.

One essential factor to a designer is that he should be able to convey precisely the colour he has selected to the painter, dyer, or printer, so that his intentions can be carried out accurately. For this a paint, ink or dye manufacturer's colour chart may be helpful in a simple case but this limits choice to a small range of colours selected by someone remote from the problem – as well as limiting the executant to materials manufactured by a particular firm. A much wider and more precise system of classification is necessary, and the one most widely adopted in the building sphere is the 'Munsell' system. This dates from the beginning of the century, although it has come into common use here only since the old Ministry of Education introduced their 'Archrome' range of colours in the early fifties. Other systems have been developed and are useful in their own fields, but in building their limitations tend to be too great for them to be useful. The British Standard (BSS 4800) uses Munsell notation.

Munsell's great advantage is that it is capable of extension as new pigments are discovered. It has no finite boundaries, recognises differences in intensity among known pigments, and can include infinite gradations of three 'dimensions' of colour, although in practice a limited series of finite steps is found adequate.

Munsell

The idea of the Munsell colour chart is that the steps or gradations of each of three dimensions of colour can be quantified, the dimensions being hue, chroma and value. Because of this, any colour can be accurately reproduced from a formula (Fig. 7.44).

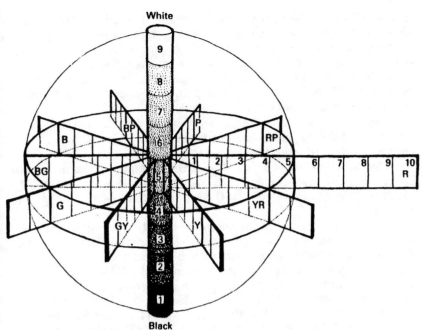

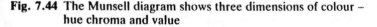

Fig. 7.44 The Munsell diagram shows three dimensions of colour – hue chroma and value

Around the equator of the figure are arranged the HUES, hue being that characteristic of colour by which we distinguish red from blue.

Chromatic colours are those with this characteristic of hue, monochromatic colours share the same hue while varying in value and chroma (which can lead to some ambiguity if the terms are not properly understood) and achromatic colours (white, grey, black) lack hue.

Instead of the three primary colours placed equally around the perimeter of the colour wheel discussed earlier, five primaries are recognised in the Munsell system – red, yellow, green, blue and purple. When these are evenly arranged around a circle a much closer approximation to the proportions of the colours present in white light is obtained. Five intermediate hues are also recognised, and steps between can be defined – usually limited to four at each stage. This means that forty different hues are immediately identifiable, with no limit to the further subdivisions that could be obtained.

Not all the hues that lie on this equator will be at their fullest intensity (unlike the colour wheel). This system takes into account the fact that with some pigments a much stronger colour can be obtained than with others. This characteristic of colour is called CHROMA and spokes radiating from the centre of the diagram bear regular marked steps indicating the chroma of the hues. At step 3, the intensity of any hue will be the same, but while some hues can reach only a limited intensity, a colour like red can be so bright that the scale of chroma projects well outside the diagram, to point 10. As new pigments are discovered, other scales can be extended.

The dullest colours, of course, are those of 'low chroma' lying at the centre of the diagram, while the brightest are those of 'high chroma' at the extremities of the radii.

The third dimension is that of VALUE (lightness or darkness) and is indicated on a scale running vertically through the centre of the diagram. White (high value) is at the top, and black (low value) at the bottom.

Any hue can have any chroma from nil to the maximum obtainable with available pigments, as well as any value between black and white, and all of these three characteristics can be quantified.

The diagram represents a three-dimensional solid – all the spaces between the arms can be filled in with possible colours.

To take examples of Munsell formulae: the first figure and letters represent the hue (with 5.0 as the purest colour) the second figure is the value, and the higher the number, the lighter the colour, and the third number is the chroma, with the highest number indicating the brightest colour.

So 5.0B7/4 is a fairly light, brightish pure blue, while 7.5R4/16 is a red very slightly on the yellow side of the pure colour, of medium value and very great intensity.

[Note: It is practically impossible to learn colour from a black and white book, and students might be well advised to provide themselves with a copy of BS 4800, or a set of manufacturers' colours in that range. Not all manufacturers indicate the Munsell reference on the chips, contenting themselves with the BS reference numbers. These give some information, but are less useful than Munsell designations, and a set bearing the latter should be obtained.]

A Munsell atlas is published, giving chips and formulae for several hundred colours, from which the ranges referred to are chosen.

While there will always be the need for the 'artist's eye' in preparing the most subtle colour schemes, the knowledge of colour available through the Munsell classification makes it possible for everyone to avoid the worst clashes. The harmonic relationship which may not be immediately apparent between 10.0YR3/2 (a brown) and 10.0YR8/4 (a beige) or between 7.5R9/2 (pale pink) and 7.5R3/12 (brick red), will be evident from their formulae. Each pair in fact shares a hue – the pairs are monochromatic and could safely (in the right location) be used together. 5.0B9/2 (duck egg blue) 7.5BG6/2 (turquoise) and 7.5G3/4 (dark green) are a harmony, with 7.5R8/4 as a contrast. The first two and the last of these four are pale colours, and the last two are rather brighter than the first two.

The name manufacturers give to colours (like the names I have used above) can be very misleading. Firms will give different names to the same colour, and the same name to different colours – so the use of names and descriptions should be avoided wherever possible, in favour of Munsell classifications.

Colour schemes

Further guidelines based on observed phenomena, which should be borne in mind by anyone putting together a colour scheme, include the points mentioned below:

1. Psychological effects ·
   (a) Some colours have the effect of apparently creating warmth while others have a cool effect. The blue/green side of the colour diagram is the cool side, while reds and oranges are categorised as 'warm'. This may be very evident where high chroma colours are used, but the phenomenon is still present at quite low intensity. It can usefully, and quite subtly, be employed by perhaps choosing a very low chroma orange instead of a neutral grey, where an effect of warmth is needed. It is often thought desirable to use warm colours in a room with a north aspect, reserving cooler ones for ones that are flooded with sunlight.
   (b) Some hues, we are told by psychologists, have a stimulating, while others have a calming, effect. Blue-greens are soothing, red purples aggressive – and knowledge of this may be important in choosing colours for a leisure centre, a workplace or a hospital waiting area, to take some obvious examples.
      This effect is related to chroma, high chromas having the greatest impact.
   (c) An effect of recession or advance is associated with particular colours. In general, warm colours advance while cool ones appear to recede – and this can affect the apparent shape of a space in which they are used. A long room will seem shorter if advancing colours are used on the short walls and cool on the long while it would appear even longer if the reverse were done. Since high chroma and low value colours can also be seen to advance, it will be seen that a dark intense red will advance most, white a pale low chroma blue will be among the most recessive colours.

The cumulative effect of (a)–(c) is shown in Fig 7.45.

2. Colour and lighting are inseparable. It is important to realise which of the selected colours will be seen in light and which in shade. If well distributed lighting is important, it may be wise to

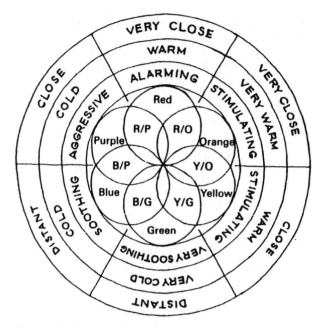

Fig. 7.45 The subtle effects colours may have are summed-up in this chart

favour high-value colours in the worst-lit areas, reserving those of lower value for well-lit spots.

On the other hand the shape of a space can be emphasised if low values are used in darker areas and high ones where it is light.

To avoid glare, it is generally advisable to paint glazing bars (internally) in very high values, and the use of high values on window cills and reveals will both improve light distribution and minimise glare.

There is a direct (if approximate) relationship between value and reflection factor. Value multiplied by value – 1 ($V(V-1)$) gives the figure – so a value of 6 is equivalent to a reflectance of about $6 \times 5 = 30$ per cent.

3. It is generally wise to reserve the highest chromas for comparatively small areas of surface – though they should be simply shaped and well proportioned ones, since they will draw the eye. As a rule of thumb (though not an unbreakable axiom) the larger the area, the lower the chroma has to be to create the same impact. This is one reason why inexperienced designers often find that colours chosen from the small chips in a colour chart are far too bright when they are used on-site. It takes a great deal of experience to appreciate the effect of a large area of a colour seen only in a small quantity.

4. A background of complementary hue (even at quite low chroma)

tends to emphasise an area of colour. The possible effect of after-images due to fatigue of the retina in the pool of complementary colour should also be taken into account. If the eye has to rest for long on a red triangle, it will later rest by 'seeing' blue-green triangles against any background. Naturally, the effect of this on a busy scheme can be most disruptive. There is also an optical illusion by which, through the juxtaposition of colours, the eye can be pursuaded to 'see' hues that are not actually present, and this effect is one to be avoided in an interior.

5. Any colour scheme which is to retain interest for any length of time needs to contain within it – and usually within a very limited palette of colours – three separate kinds of contrast:

(*a*)   Contrast of hue. A scheme made up entirely of harmonious colours may be very restful, but will lack 'bite' and the selected colours will lose their impact. A contrasting hue sets off and intensifies the harmony and rests the eye. Note that the harmony should consist of DIFFERENT hues – monochromatic colours will have less impact. Three colours in harmony plus one contrast are often a good basis for a colour scheme.

(*b*)   Contrast of value. There should always be some variation between darker and lighter colours. A subtle variation between values 4 and 6 may be more effective than one between values 2 and 8, but contrast should always be present among the values of a scheme.

(*c*)   Contrast of chroma. A scheme consisting entirely of saturated colours would be naïve and crude, while one made up from low chroma hues could well be monotonous. High-chroma colours may of course be avoided entirely if the scheme is intended to provide a background (in a museum, say) but some variation in this respect is essential if the effect is not to be banal.

Four colours could be chosen which provided among them all these kinds of contrast, and which took into account all the points above.

For the long, narrow foyer of a hotel, in which a lively but sophisticated effect was required, and where apparent shortening of the space seemed sensible, the colours chosen might be:

Floor	8.75YR/2/2	(dark brown) warm, low value, low chroma.
End walls	7.5R3/10	(rich red) warm, low value, high chroma.
Upholstery	10.0YR7/6	(gold) neutral, medium value, medium chroma.
Ceiling	10.0YR9/2	(the same) high value, low chroma.
Long walls	10.0PB6/2	(dull blue) cool, medium value, low chroma.

Having taken all the above points regarding the choice of colour into account, it is easy to fall into the twin traps of over elaboration on the one hand or excessive austerity on the other. The unity of the scheme can be destroyed, or at least severely damaged, if too many changes and variations are allowed to intrude, while the whole effect will be boring in the extreme if no variety at all is permitted. An approach which will avoid either of these pitfalls would be (in the case of the hotel referred to above) to limit the 'palette' of hues for the hotel to the four included in the foyer, plus a further two in harmony with the blue, and then to use these colours in various combinations of value and chroma, throughout the building. A surprising amount of variation of effect would prove attainable, yet the entire scheme would have an overall unity and house character – and accessories moved from one room to another would have a good chance of looking satisfactory in their new surroundings.

This approach of preparing a limited range of colours for a job also takes care automatically of the view from one space into another (perhaps through an open door) which may often be overlooked. In particular in the small job, such as a single house, one simple scheme for the whole will virtually always be more successful than schemes for individual spaces prepared piecemeal.

A prized possession, such as a painting, is often chosen to 'key' a scheme. Though this can be very successful if the picture is set at the focal point of the space, it needs to be done with care. Firstly, the colours need to be used in similar proportions and relationships to those in which they appear in the original if distortion is to be avoided, and secondly the rule about the areas over which colours are used must be conformed to. Each colour to be used over a larger area than appears on the original will need to be reduced in chroma accordingly.

Conclusion

In the case of any one of the aspects of good design that have been discussed, complications are introduced if the object being designed is three-dimensional. A good poster design is simpler to achieve than a good shop window display, for example. Any object which can be seen from a variety of points of view must be satisfactory from all of them, and additionally it is an advantage if there is some element of change and surprise (within the overall unity of the concept) as the viewer moves.

The design of a building, which besides having depth will not only be seen from many external angles but from internal ones too – in which the observer will move about – quite clearly demands the careful exercise of well developed aesthetic judgement if a satisfactory visual solution is to be found. Producing an aesthetically successful building design is a most demanding intellectual exercise.

The reader will therefore appreciate that although there are well understood rules of aesthetics, outlined here, whose application to simple objects may seem a simple matter, the design of buildings is of such complexity as to require a very sophisticated eye.

It is particularly important that 'ground rules' should be established for the particular project, and kept to throughout, if unity is to result. It is vital that the overall massing, proportion and balance of the design should be understood and respected by everyone in the design team. In particular, it is essential that the leadership of the design team by a single mind, in this respect as in all others, should be accepted.

Of all the team, it is only the architect who can claim a training and experience specifically aimed to prepare him for this task, and his claim to such leadership is, for this reason, a very strong one.

[Note: Rules are made to be broken. No sooner are guidelines promulgated than some high-flyer displays his genius by successfully ignoring them. Few of us can claim genius, though, and the great majority of designers ignore such rules at their peril.]

Chapter 8

Synthesis

It may seem comparatively simple to look at one aspect of a design problem at a time, as I have done in previous chapters. It is when these varied components of the whole have to be related and kept in balance that the complications proliferate.

If any control is to be kept over the way in which the solution emerges, one very early step must be to determine which particular elements in this unique problem are actually the most critical and far-reaching in their effects. These aspects of the problem can and should then be the subject of early and detailed examination and decision, and provided these first decisions are taken logically, and the assessment of their importance has been accurate, it will rarely, if ever, be necessary to reconsider them during the development of the design.

For example, in the case of a theatre the functional requirements of the stage, and the sight lines to be provided in the auditorium, would in all probability be considered so important that firm decisions on these points had to be arrived at before any other aspect of the design received detailed consideration. The nature of the facilities needed in these respects would depend on the nature of the theatrical experience being sought: proscenium, thrust and studio stages make quite different demands. Considerable research into these requirements would have to precede any thought of construction or massing. It should be appreciated, though, that it is difficult to take such decisions in total isolation. Decisions will be affected by the designer's previous experience and his generalised understanding of the constructional techniques which are available to him. In one way it is fortunate that he finds it impossible to clear his mind of such ideas – they tend to influence the taking of sensible decisions. They might also, however, induce him to abandon as impractical some device he has not actually come across in practice, and often to fail to innovate when this might be a fruitful path. In Shakespeare's day, or even the eighteenth century, the designer of a theatre could not envisage the possibility of the big clear spans taken for granted by his successor today. He would automatically dismiss from his mind a tentative solution he believed to be impractical. The danger is that an architect may have so definite an idea of what can and cannot be done that he fails to think laterally and neglects the endeavour to innovate in response to new problems.

If a design that clearly solves the functional problem seems at first not to be capable of realisation, it should not, of course, be abandoned on that account until rigorous evaluation has proved that this is indeed the case.

The architect will, similarly, be aware of the massing likely to be generated by the arrangement of accommodation he is contemplating. He ought never, in any case, to visualise the building purely in terms of a plan, even though that is a useful shorthand way of noting his ideas. A building is a three-dimensional object, and that is how the designer will think of it – many of his drawings will be thumbnail perspective sketches, during the design stage. This feeling for the massing, and the ways in which it can be expressed may be practically subconscious, but it will influence the way in which ideas are developed. The architect will begin to experiment with alternative arrangements, to see what their implications would be. The fact that function, in this particular case, is regarded as the most vital ingredient of the design, does not imply that nothing else is of any importance at all – but that other points may have to be compromised before the way the building works. Ideally, as we have seen, the building eventually provided should present a perfect solution from the aesthetic and technical, as well as the functional viewpoint.

On a city centre site, for a prestige building, it is possible that appearance might be thought all-important. This would certainly have been true fifty years or so ago – though it is less common today, as we have all been trained to believe that the appearance of the building should result from the function and construction rather than predetermine those parts of design. Nevertheless, on some important sites the height or impact of a building may be of great importance to the townscape as a whole. Still, the functional requirements and method of construction would not be wholly ignored in determining the building's appearance (else what was built would rank as a 'folly') but might be modified for the sake of the external impression to be created.

Again, if the building was a commercial one, such as an office block intended for letting, the critical factor so far as the developer was concerned would probably be the return on investment to be expected. Much careful assessment of cost limits to balance capital expenditure, maintenance costs and rents would be involved. Even so, it would be realised that an inconvenient or outstandingly ugly block would be less likely to attract tenants prepared to pay high rents, while one that stood empty because it was too expensive would (in any normal economic situation) be a poor investment.

Failure to analyse such problems adequately can make a difficult design problem virtually insoluble. If the theatre designer has preconceived ideas of what the eventual building should look like he may find it impossible to provide a good theatrical machine. If the prestige building were too closely tied to cost considerations the aesthetic scope could be unduly constrained, and if the office block put external impact before the provision of lettable space it might prove uncommercial.

Whichever aspect of the design is accepted as being, in the unique circumstances, of primary importance, a good many rough sketches will be made, on the lines of Figs. 8.1, 8.2, 8.3 and so on, to assess the implications of alternative strategies before decisions are reached. It will be rare for the conditions to be so tight that only one solution is viable, and there are distinct advantages in keeping a number of options open to as late in the development stage as possible. This avoids the designer becoming wedded to a particular line of thought, throws up a number of variations at each stage for consideration, and is likely to produce a better eventual answer to the problem.

Example

It will be useful to follow the way in which one simple design is developed as an example of the technique recommended.

The designer will inspect the site, refer to examples, consult the planning authority and question the client, to expand the commission into a 'brief' as described in Chapter 3. He then finds he is faced with a very large amount of information, clamouring for attention. If he is to respond in any intelligent fashion, he has to begin by sorting out priorities, in order that he can work systematically and logically.

In the case of the simple factory building which has been considered in earlier chapters, it seems evident that the convenient arrangement of the accommodation will be of the first importance, with simple and easily maintained construction a close second. Discussion with the client might establish a hierarchy of requirements much as follows:

1. Simple and logical plan.
2. Good working conditions.
3. Security.
4. Easy and safe access for people and goods.

5. Simple construction, which could easily be adapted at a later date.
6. Straightforward, efficient services, with easy access for maintenance.
7. To be as far as possible maintenance free.
8. Appearance.
9. Good use of the site.
10. Cost.

Cost and programme

The quantity surveyor will be asked at once to begin preparation of a cost plan, on the lines described in Chapter 12, which can be used to monitor likely costs throughout the design stage. Meanwhile, in consultation with everyone who is to be involved, the architect has to prepare a programme (probably in the form of a bar chart) to show the dates by which certain critical stages of design will be reached. He may well, for example, indicate the dates by which all critical data must be obtained, when initial advice from consultants will be needed, when the structural system is to have been selected, and a cut-off date for design decisions, allowing time for the preparation of presentation drawings for the agreed submission date. In addition, times can be pencilled-in for discussions with the planning authority, factory inspector, and so on. This programme allows everyone to know what is required of him as well as when he can rely on being provided with information he needs.

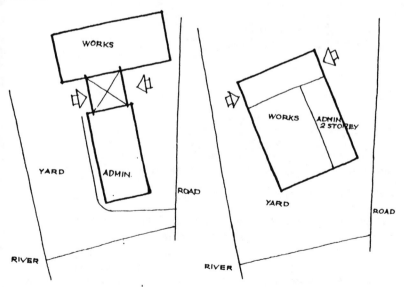

Fig. 8.1 Early ideas

Accommodation

The designers can now begin by examining the accommodation required in some detail, since this is considered critical. Here, it emerges that the spaces needed can be divided between two classes: workshops and stores on the one hand and reception and offices on the other. The first group require good headroom, clear spans, and a controlled environment, while the second are more domestic in scale but need a higher standard of finishes.

Plan and massing

One early decision to be taken should be between enclosing both sets of rooms within a single block (perhaps planning the offices and so on on two floors) and articulating the two groups separately. Figure 8.1 indicates the way in which these options could be explored. In the first case, the ratio of external envelope to enclosed volume would be advantageous, so cost may be kept down and heat loss minimised. It would, however, be necessary to provide stairs. The second option seems more logical, and will be more readily understood by passers-by. It may be possible, because of limited spans in the office area, to use lighter and cheaper construction there. Unless the two sets of accommodation turn out to produce masses of approximately equal volume, making for difficulties with the massing, the second option seems, on balance, to offer the greatest advantages. Sketches to indicate the sorts of massing that might be produced will be made (Fig. 8.2).

Fig. 8.2 The development of the massing

Once this division of the accommodation has been decided upon, further sketches to consider alternative plan forms which would follow the requirements of the circulation diagram will be made. Such sketches are the designer's note for his own benefit, and need not make more than a single point apiece. They will not have to be read by anyone else. He will note the effect of the orientation of the site and the desirability of preserving trees and opening the stream to view, but will recognise that these points (unless, indeed they are requirements of the planning authority) are to have low priority. He will continue to think three-dimensionally, and thumbnail sketches of massing will accompany any indicative plans.

Most designers would at this stage prepare several different tentative ideas, any of which could be developed into a workable scheme, and between which a choice will be made on technical and aesthetic grounds later.

Construction

Little further progress can be made without a firm idea of the kind of construction to be employed. Sketches such as Fig. 3.6, in Chapter 3, show the kind of exploratory work that might be done. In any individual case, there are always a number of viable options available, which should be explored in some detail before a logical decision is taken. This decision may be influenced by cost factors, and reference to the cost plan in consultation with the quantity surveyor will be part of the process. Cost should not be allowed the key role, however as there are other factors to be taken into account. Conformity with the prevailing materials of other buildings in the area, the kinds of details that will be produced, maintenance requirements and the possibilities of future adaptation all need to be considered.

Three constructions, from among the many available, which might be examined for the factory would be:

1. A timber portal frame, clad with framed timber panels, which might seem appropriate for what is in reality a specialised joiner's shop.
2. A light steel frame clad with sandwich panels and patent glazing would quickly be erected, and would conform in general to the appearance of the buildings across the stream.
3. Loadbearing brickwork, carrying light steel joists and a flat deck of channel-edged wood wool would be in keeping with the domestic buildings across the street.

Optimum bay sizes will be explored, as well as the standards of insulation which can be reached (and the means by which they can be achieved). The opportunities for alteration of the building later, and the extent of maintenance required, will also be assessed. This may be a lengthy and rigorous process.

Eventually, a decision will be agreed. In this case, we will assume that the third of the options listed has been selected. Standard details for openings, eaves, foundations and other critical points of the design need to be made, to establish the relationships of the structures to one another and the grid, and the bay size to be used. These are a necessary basis for the actual preparation of a plan.

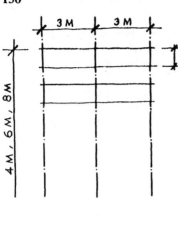

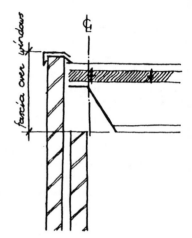

Fig. 8.3 Constructional constraints must be taken into account

Fig. 8.3 shows the kind of framework that will be established.

Services

Meanwhile, some consideration will be given by consultants to the services needed to provide the environmental conditions asked for, and the space allowances to be made for them. The demands of dust extraction and humidity control will be given special consideration by the engineer, who will estimate plant and duct sizes and the optimum siting in relationship to machines. A decision will be taken as to whether hot and cold water services, as well as heating and wastes are to be concealed in ducts, and if so how large these should be, what access they require, and the recommended positions for them.

The requirements with regard to natural and artificial lighting will also be considered, to establish guidelines for the design. The extent of roof light provision, or the preferred depth of offices, might be stated.

The choice of fuel for the plant also needs to be considered early. In present economic conditions, gas might seem an obvious choice, and it is certainly a convenient choice for the designer since it allows him to site the plant room wherever he likes. The client might very well, however, wish to retain the option of a change to solid fuel later, if conditions were to change, and particularly if the site were in a mining area, where public policy might be to offer incentives for the use of solid fuel. This would mean that the siting of the plant room became critical, and that space and access for a future fuel store had to be allowed for. Such implications would need to be considered carefully, and clearly explained to the client so that he can make the decision. In the present case we will assume he has decided in all the circumstances he wishes to preserve the option.

Further attention will also have to be paid to the drainage of the site. Consultation with the town hall may be needed, to establish whether surface water may be drained into the stream (which may well depend on avoiding pollution) and it is possible that difficult relative levels might create problems – though in the event this does not seem to be so.

Since a three-phase electrical supply will be needed, details of switchroom requirements will also be required now.

Finishes

There are also less vital but still influential details to be considered: the demands made upon the finishes should be scheduled so that decisions upon the materials to be selected can be made (possibly through 'brainstorming' (see Ch. 2)). Their choice might affect the sketch details previously prepared, which have to be modified as may be necessary before detailed planning, so that the right allowances for thicknesses, fixings and cover strips are made.

Development

At this stage, it will be remembered, there is still no finished plan of the building – only two or three ideas that have been taken little beyond the 'feasibility study' stage.

Now, however, sufficient information is available to allow a plan to be prepared. This will accept the bay size and relationships between the parts which have been determined, and make the correct functional allowances for the services.

Even if the first idea developed looks workable, it is generally wise to develop more than one of the tentative sketches. This gives an opportunity for comparisons, and often allows a fresh new solution to emerge as the strong points of each proposal are identified and developed.

The developing plan will be accompanied by thumbnail sketches showing the general massing and architectural expression, so that the arrangement that is best from every point of view can be chosen. At the same time, attention will be paid to the best use that can be made of the site, and a number of alternative arrangements may be evaluated from this point of view (Figs. 8.4, 8.5).

Fig. 8.4 Will the foyer appear welcoming?

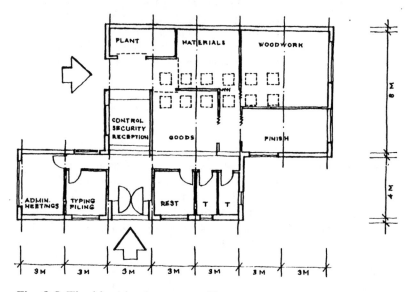

Fig. 8.5 The ideas begin to crystallise

Eventually it will seem clear that the optimum arrangement has been found, and firmer and more detailed drawings will be made.

Costs

Cost will, every time a decision between alternatives has to be made, be one of the factors to be taken into account, but it should rarely be the most important guideline in any particular case. Constant reference to the cost plan will ensure that the architect is alerted to any danger of overspending soon enough to adjust his proposals or ask for further instructions (see Ch. 12).

Evaluation

Before he is in a position to make recommendations of a scheme to his client, the designer has to put in hand a stringent evaluation of his proposals. He may well ask colleagues to assist him in this, since a

Fig. 8.6 Designing is done in three dimensions, plan, section and elevation are just handy ways of conveying ideas

fresh mind may note some point that over-familiarity is causing him to overlook. The objective will be to identify every point on which compromises have been made, and to be confident that in every feature of this kind the less important factor has given way to the more important, rather than the reverse.

Every satisfactory building, irrespective of priorities, ought to share certain characteristics. It is a worthwhile exercise to consider whether buildings with which one is familiar do, in fact, satisfy such criteria:

1. The organisation of the plan should be simple and easily understood and used, and waste space should be avoided.
2. Well chosen materials should be used in a straightforward way.
3. The appearance should be unified and well proportioned, and should express the internal organisation of the spaces and the way in which the building is constructed.
4. Good use should be made of the features of the site.
5. Any decoration should be well chosen and placed where it enhances and draws attention to the good structural features of the design.

Conclusions

The case described is, of course, a comparatively simple one, chosen because it could be explained briefly. The design is unlikely to involve a large team, and the objectives are clear-cut.

Where a large team of specialists is engaged on a design, or where there are conflicting aims, the development of the design might be less trouble-free, and it becomes important to establish stages of design and the extent of delegated responsibility for decisions.

For example, one can envisage the case of a theatre complex to be built on a tight city site. Because the site is small and the character of the area urban, it will be necessary for the building to largely cover the ground: perhaps this will not permit the optimum arrangement of the foyers and booking area. It is possible that an obtrusive stage tower must be provided, though the instinct of the architect is to concentrate on expressing the characteristic shape of the auditorium. Again, the ventilation requirements might threaten to become a dominant feature of the composition, or the need for fire stopping make open planned circulation spaces unattainable.

In any case of this kind, what appears to be an impasse can often be better resolved by making a virtue of necessity than by trying to get round the problem. Theatre is a visual art, and clearly the appearance of a theatre matters – but cannot the interesting relationship between tower and auditorium be exploited as easily as the auditorium alone? If the ventilation ducts are obtrusive, can they not become features of the design in their own right? Being practical does not debar an object from being attractive to look at.

Often preconceived ideas lie behind apparent difficulties of the kind described. It has been stressed before that a designer has to avoid forming ideas before he has fully analysed the problem, if he is to hope to be successful. Provided everyone concerned with the design has a clear grasp of the hierarchy of requirements, and is prepared to let this control his decisions, there is no reason why the design process of even the most complicated building should not run smoothly.

It is, naturally, beyond the skill of any individual to consider every aspect of the design at the same time. The evaluation stage of the process is, for this reason, essential, and it must be carried out ruthlessly. The design must be tested against the mandatory and desirable requirements in order of their priority, and it ought really, if a major fault is found, to be abandoned.

This situation should be rare indeed, if the design has proceeded systematically and there has been continuous evaluation. If it should occur, however, slight adjustment is less likely to correct the fault than abandonment of all work done subsequently to the error creeping in: everything which follows has to be assumed to be based, to at least some extent, on the false assumption. This is a major reason for stressing the importance of evaluation as an essential strand throughout design, rather than as a discrete stage.

There is, however, a final stage of testing of the ideas beyond what could reasonably be attempted earlier. Mock-up rooms may be made, or models tested in wind tunnels, for example, to confirm that working space is adequate or that undesirable turbulence will not be created. Similarly, more detailed cost assessments might now be prepared. If adequate thought has gone into development, such tests will merely provide final assurance that important objectives are being achieved.

Presentation

Finally, the design has to be presented to client, public and interested authorities in realistic, honest and understandable form (see Ch. 9).

The drawings and the report have to draw together not only what the proposed building would be like, but also the reasons which have influenced its design, and it will be essential to convey clearly where the priorities were perceived to lie.

Chapter 9

Communication

The characteristics of effective communication

Anyone who has to amuse a child for a day, or entertain a visitor from abroad, or visit an elderly relative in hospital knows about the obstacles that can hamper effective communication. Automatically one speaks to the child in a simple vocabulary, and explains things by reference to his known experience; one takes care that the foreigner is actually understanding what is said and not just nodding polite agreement; one turns the hospital conversation to the life of the ward, the invalid's progress – or the football team in the outside world that he is known to support.

In other words, where there are known conversational hazards to be overcome we take pains to cope with them. Most difficulties in communication arise because we are insufficiently aware of similar kinds of difficulty.

The theory of communication is an attempt to explain the constituent parts of successful communication, and the difficulties that can hinder it. It provides useful guidance to efficiency in the exchange of information.

Effective communication depends as much upon the recipient as upon the originator of a message. This idea is familiar to anyone concerned with radio: there is little point in a broadcast, no matter how informative and skilfully presented it may be, unless the potential audience has receivers tuned to the right wavelength. However beautifully music is performed, and however sophisticated the

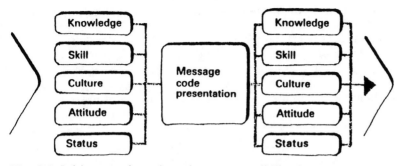

Fig. 9.1 Initiator and receiver share responsibility for effective communication

transmission equipment, the quality can be ruined by poor reception, over-amplification, or incorrect balance at the ʳeceiving end (Fig. 9.1).

Five characteristics have been identified as needing to be common to both ends of the communication chain. These are: skills, attitudes, culture, knowledge and status. A discrepancy in any one of these areas – or, perhaps more importantly, a failure to appreciate that one of the characteristics is not present at the same level at the distant end of the chain – is sufficient to endanger the satisfactory passage of information. The message may be misunderstood, without either party realising that this is the case, or even that such a thing is possible. Figure 9.2 illustrates this point.

Fig. 9.2 Any factor which interferes with clear communication is 'noise'

Failures of communication too small to be immediately apparent are frighteningly common. An architect may have the clearest idea of what he means by 'good bricklaying' – a perception of quality. To him it may mean a particular degree of unevenness in the texture and colour of the wall, that he associates with traditional brick buildings. To the bricklayer, on the other hand, whose training has been concerned with obtaining the greatest possible degree of uniformity and strength, the phrase may mean something quite different. To someone else it may be the brickwork which is put up most quickly and at least cost. Each of these people would take his definition of the same words so much for granted, that he would never question that everyone else used the phrase with the same connotation. It is only by appreciating a difference in attitude and education that one begins to see the possibility of confusion.

Even within a common language the same words may mean different things to different professional groups because the objectives that seem automatic and unquestionable to one may differ significantly from those of another.

Miscommunications seem to be impossible to avoid. They occur even between the members of one family, one school class, one team in an office. We should be aware of the situations in which they are likely to arise, and aim to eradicate as many as possible. We must aim, too, to identify the misunderstandings that DO occur early enough to avoid escalating consequences.

In writing this, I have to bear this in mind. It is easy for me to fall into the habit of assuming that I have more in common with my readers than is actually the case. I spent a good many years in architects' offices – and that, I expect, is where most of my readers are employed. I could easily forget that I have more recently worked for several years in an educational institution – and that in any case, architects' offices vary a good deal. My definition of excellence in architecture may not be shared by those who read this book, and if a difference in objectives remains undiscovered you may easily and understandably get the wrong end of the stick as to what I'm driving at.

We musn't forget that there's a generation gap, too.

Not only is it necessary for me to appreciate the potential gulf, – the reader has to do so, too. I am an architect and an academic writing from a lifetime's (possibly circumscribed) experience; you are looking forward to a career in a world that may be very different from mine. I shall hope I have explained myself, and you will hope that you have understood me correctly: we shall each recognise that an effort is required on both sides.

Skills

It should be obvious that a proper grasp of the techniques involved is essential to the proper transmission of messages, and to their interpretation, too. Speaking face to face, we need to share a language, we need good diction and sharp hearing, and we need to pay attention. The listener needs to want to hear and understand, and to concentrate on doing so. Knowing *how* to pay attention is a skill to be acquired, too.

If we send written messages, legible writing is essential, and if we receive them we need to be able to read. Making drawings involves knowledge of graphical language as well as skill in draughtsmanship. Reading drawings, too, is a skill that has to be mastered. Ability to handle telephone and telex, computer terminal and microfiche is basic, too, these days. Towards the end of this chapter, some of the particular languages used in building communications, and their place in our repertoire, are discussed in a little more detail.

Culture

One difficulty that can hamper communication with a visitor from abroad, plainly, is the lack of a common cultural background. This is something different from lack of a shared language. It is the lack of a common frame of reference for our allusions.

We may be less aware that a similar phenomenon can occur within our own society, yet this can be the case. Two people may share a knowledge of building, have equivalent status in their separate fields, have well developed communication skills, both be British, and share the same priorities, yet because one moves in a circle interested in classical music, theatre and squash while the other follows soccer and likes a pint in the working men's club on Saturday evening, they may use terms and allusions that are lost upon one another.

This gulf can open between different age groups, between north and south, between men and women. Our experience and the context in which we have obtained it has programmed our responses in a particular way – and it will, when everything is taken into account, be a way that is unique to the individual.

Knowledge

We often make a facile assumption that our level of knowledge, and our field of knowledge, are common property, when this is not actually so. Two equally well educated people can find a chasm dividing them when it is discovered that one is a technologist and the other a designer. Each tends to expect the other to share his background, his objectives and his system of priorities, even though thought should reveal that this could hardly be expected to be the case. This assumption may lead us to despise the other party for gaps in his expected understanding – but one should never undervalue a protagonist in these circumstances. His ignorance of material that seems to oneself as instinctive as digestion is probably matched by gaps in one's own equipment that seem to HIM equally culpable. It is more productive to respect one another for the specialised depth of knowledge each can bring to the problem.

In a design team the heating engineer, the sociologist, the landscape architect may each have a contribution to make. Each profession has its own jargon – and the team can only cooperate properly if each makes a deliberate effort to understand and be understood. You know that you know less about structures than the structural engineer – equally you must expect that he knows less about your particular field than you do – and think none the less of him for it.

Status

Anyone who is conscious of inferiority in a particular situation, whether that is due to his lack of experience, his lack of skill or to his position in some real or fancied 'pecking order' – or, indeed, anyone who looks down on a person with whom he hopes to communicate – has to make a special effort to understand and be understood. The perceived discrepancy in status is a hindrance.

A child gives great weight to what is said by a respected adult, and because of this he learns values and attitudes on which to base his own in later life. The apprentice system depended on a similar effect. We tend to pay less attention to the office boy's dicta than to those of the bosses. We may fail to appreciate the wisdom of our elders if we fail to respect them. Without commenting on the sociology of such situations, it is clear that these are all operations of a single mechanism: that our comprehension and wish to accept what is said is affected by the relative positions of originator and receiver of a message in a hierarchy. This is a phenomenon to which we need to give attention.

I am very conscious as I write that what appears in print gains status from that fact. I wonder whether students I have met over the years, and readers to whom I am only a printed word, will attach the same importance to what I say.

Because our perception of our own status and our understanding of the way we are seen by others – as well as our perception of others – affect both our confidence in ourselves and our trust in colleagues, we have a duty to take as objective a view as possible of collaborations if they are to reach their full potential usefulness.

Attitudes

Far-reaching differences in our responses to particular situations, including our ranking of priorities and our scales of values, constitute the fifth potential hurdle to be overcome if perfect understanding of one another is to be within reach. If the person with whom we are attempting to communicate has a point of view basically different from our own, misunderstandings are virtually inevitable.

It is natural for us to assume that our ingrained prejudices (and we all have them, whether we like to believe it or not) are shared by the community as a whole. A moment's detached thought indicates that this is NOT the case. Another difficulty can be that we tend to attribute to an individual attitudes we believe to be endemic to his group – even though we do not ourselves share them – and anxiety not to offend can lead to a labyrinth of misunderstanding.

Noise

The kinds of hindrance or obstacle to clear mutual understanding to which I have referred are known as 'noise', and it is a characteristic of noise that we don't realise it is present unless it overwhelms us. If you live in a town you have to *listen* to realise the constant background of sound from traffic against which you live your life. The same is true in the country, of the barrage of sound from animals, birds and tractors. In each case, the noise is enough to disturb, if one wishes to listen to the tick of a clock.

In the same way we struggle along against a noisy interference of misunderstanding in our communications with one another. We fail to notice that someone is not picking up our allusions to pop culture; we in our turn fail to respond to a metaphor drawn from the casino. Our vocabulary acquires overtones and implications which are understood by a limited circle but not outside it.

The man who said Britain and America were divided by a common language was drawing attention to the way this unconscious barrier can be more insidious than an expected one, and it is a point of which we would do well to be aware.

Channels of communication

Communications do not only pass through words and drawings, of course. Smell, taste and touch all convey a message as well as sight and sound.

Advertisers are adept at adding evocative scents or allusive names to their products. All the associations which are called up become part of the message – so it is not only the content of a drawing but also the professionalism of its presentation which may lead to accurate interpretation of the draughtsman's intentions.

Similarly, the letterhead and the quality of the paper in a letter begin to communicate with the reader before a word is taken in.

Any sensory deficiency will cause noise, and so will any deficiency in skill, or lack of experience, in creating or interpreting sensory signals. An apparently instinctive ability to negotiate, or get on with the other party, or deal with staff, may be largely based on skill in these areas.

We can usually choose the most appropriate channel to use for a particular message, but need to take into account that that very choice may convey something. A solicitor's letter may say exactly, in words, what we might put into a note or a 'phone call, but will be treated much more seriously. An engraved invitation is more impressive than a scrawled note to the same effect – yet we would rather have a brief handwritten note from an admired personality, than a reproduced handout.

Structure

The message itself, additionally, needs to be carefully structured if it is to be read as intended. The initiator has first to think out what he has to convey, so that he can make an unambiguous statement. This will involve determination of the main point and ancilliary points to be made, identification of material that is only explanatory, and simplification of any reasoning to be presented so that the argument can be followed clearly.

When this is done, the material has to be encoded – for even words are a code (a well understood one, it is true) to convey meaning from one mind to another. If drawings are to be used, there may be a choice of style to be made between orthographic and three-dimensional presentation. In many cases, a decision as to whether drawings with notes or illustrated text is more appropriate may have to be made. In every case, the choice should be determined by what will be most readily understood by the recipient, rather than by the particular communication skills possessed by the originator. One would not present a sectional elevation to a four-year-old, not annotations in Chinese to a Westerner, though both these methods may need to be used on other occasions.

When preparing drawings there is a great temptation to include a great deal of extraneous material in order to show that everything has been considered. The firm making the windows, however, does not need to have his drawings cluttered up with information regarding the wall into which they are to be fixed (although the designer, the detailer and the quantity surveyor – to say nothing of the erector, will of course need this information). What the manufacturer needs is a clear drawing showing the sizes of the windows and their construction, nothing more.

This material will be less liable to misinterpretation because it will be easy to read. A special drawing should be made.

The 'need to know' principle was conceived to limit the dissemination of secret information, and I would not wish it to be thought I advocated secrecy between the team producing a building. The application of the principle to building information, though, can cut out duplication – and with it the chances of conflicting data – and can mean that each party has clear information to suit his needs, and has no need to plough through a mountain of unnecessary material.

Analysis of the message to be conveyed, and choice of the most

suitable method of transmission, are so important for the success of
the whole project that they should consciously be carried out and not
allowed to be a matter of unthinking habit.

The architectural technician as a communicator

The analysis on p. 7 of the role of an architectural technician makes
it quite clear that his greatest importance is as a skilled gatherer,
presenter and transmitter of information. Whether he is scheduling the
needs of a client, surveying available relevant structural techniques,
preparing production documents, or charting feedback from the
occupiers of a completed building, his prime role is to analyse and
present the material concerned so that it is immediately assimilable.
This will often involve apparently very simple presentation – but
presentation that can only be achieved on the basis of sophisticated
understanding of the purpose for which the information is required,
and of the means of presentation available.

In this section of the book, it is necessary to range rather beyond
the design stage of the project, since the functions of the architectural
technician in communication run throughout the job, and it seems
arbitrary to single out one stage alone.

Methods of communication in building

Figure 9.3 schedules the means of communication generally used in
building, and the uses to which they are commonly put. As has already
been pointed out, habit should not prevail; careful selection is vital.

The list is not exclusive, and there may well be occasions for
everything from the proverbial scribble on the back of an envelope to
an oil landscape, or from a telex message to a careful prose evocation
of atmosphere. Every case will be different and should be separately
considered.

It may often fall to the architectural technician to recommend or
simply to adopt the most suitable means in each case.

Drawings
There are many excellent books on draughtsmanship, and it is to be
assumed that every architectural technician takes pride in his skill in
this field – it is, after all, a basic part of his professional equipment.
This is not an appropriate place for tips on drawing.

What IS necessary, however, is to examine the various kinds of
drawing so as to provide a basis for decisions as to when each can
most appropriately be used.

BS 1192 is, of course, the useful basic reference for this topic.

164

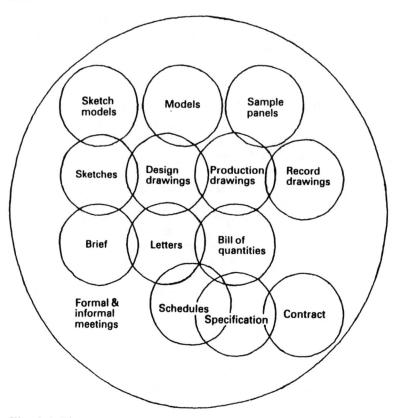

Fig. 9.3 The common methods of communication in use in the building industry

Sketch drawings

The sketch drawing, to be effective, is possibly the most difficult drawing one might be called upon to produce in an architect's office. The skill required is compounded partly of natural talent, and partly of fluency resulting from extensive practice. The sketch gives an accurate idea of the general lines of a building (or a feature; or the massing of a group); of the relationship of light and dark, enclosed or open spaces – but it gives this information without any commitment to detail, and the statement must therefore be very simply made, so that the reader appreciated the nature of the information which is being presented.

A good sketch will consist of few lines, but those lines will be confidently and clearly drawn, they will be accurately placed, and they will have been carefully selected to convey the essence of the point being made (Fig. 9.4).

Given these characteristics, a good sketch is an efficient means of

Fig. 9.4 A sketch to make a single point will do so best if it is not elaborated

conveying a simple message. Unfortunately, too many sketches obscure more than they clarify.

Too many ambiguous (or even meaningless) lines, concentration on non-essentials or the attempt to get across more than one point in a single sketch, can destroy the effectiveness of the technique. Sketches should convey accurate though simple information. The point to be made must be thought out before pencil is put to paper, and the simplest method of making that point selected. It may often be necessary to make and discard preliminary attempts.

The term 'sketch' is usually taken to mean a freehand drawing made without the use of instruments, and a drawing made rapidly as a memorandum of a particular point. Such drawings are of the greatest value during the development of a design and will usually only circulate within the design team (or indeed be made for the originator's own use).

It is valuable to develop the ability to produce good sketches. As I have said, this demands practice, and students may find it useful to start by making sketches of observed buildings and details, trying to set down their most important characteristics as economically as possible.

Figure 9.5 shows how this can be done. A soft pencil or a felt-tip or fibre-tip pen works well.

A sketch design is a different kind of drawing entirely (see 'design drawings' p. 169). This is a persentation of the results of very considerable development work and if it is prepared in a manner that

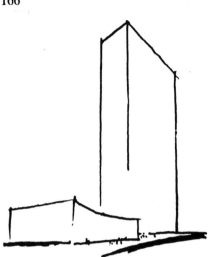

Fig. 9.5 Making quick sketches from observation involves picking out the most important characteristics of the subject

Fig. 9.6 This drawing is effective because it is simple

is evidently rapid, the impression of lack of consideration can all too easily be created. A sketch design brochure can, however, usefully include a number of sketch views to show the impact of the proposed development on its surroundings from various vantage points as is

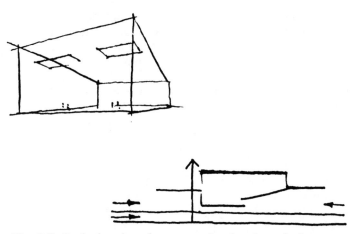

Fig. 9.7 Such sketches show very simply why a design was selected

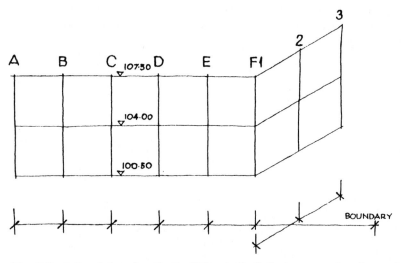

Fig. 9.8 A 'key' drawing that will control all that comes after it needs to be simple but very accurate if it is to be authoritative

shown in Fig. 9.6, or to explain the thinking behind the proposals (Fig. 9.7)

Key drawings

As firm decisions are taken, in developing the design – with regard to structural grid size, or the placing of the building on the site, perhaps – it is appropriate that drawings should be prepared and circulated within the design team, to ensure that everyone is aware of the decision, and working within the imposed constraints.

Eventually, a key grid drawing to which all details can be referenced gives a vital framework to the set of production drawings, assists setting out on-site, and can prevent ambiguous (and even mutually incompatible) dimensioning of a kind that is still often the cause of disputes and additional expense.

A drawing of this kind should be very simple indeed, conveying a very small amount of information, but it should be clear that that information overrides what may appear on other documents (Fig. 9.8).

A bold ink presentation should be chosen.

Survey and record drawings

All drawings which record fact, as opposed to explaining a proposal, should be comprehensive and accurate. They will be relied on by a variety of people as a basis for their actions, and it is inapt to include supposition and fact on the same drawing. One deviation from this principle which is common and useful, however, is the plotting of interpolated contours on to a survey plan. In such a case it should be made clear that while the spot levels have been accurately obtained, the contours are an approximation, included to show the general character of the levels in an easily read way.

Since drawings of this kind are usually very intricate, they can be surprisingly difficult to read unless attention is paid to determine which features should be emphasised. Considerable variety in weight of line can assist legibility (Fig. 9.9).

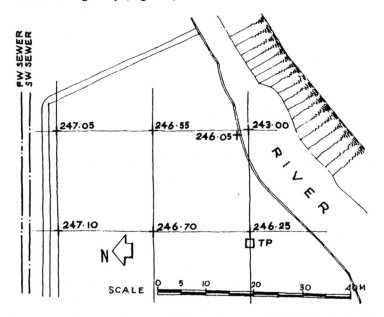

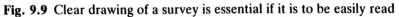

Fig. 9.9 Clear drawing of a survey is essential if it is to be easily read

It is, above all, imperative that record drawings should not only be accurate but that the date and conditions to which they refer should be very clearly indicated. For this reason the practice of revising such drawings by updating the negative (which would be entirely acceptable in the case of production drawings) should be avoided. If a fresh drawing to indicate a new set of conditions is necessary an entirely new negative should be prepared. These drawings should be in ink, clearly dated, and provided with drawn scales.

Building owners' handbook

If the documents provided to the purchaser of a car are compared to those which generally accompany a new building, it is at once apparent that we pay inadequate attention to the needs of building owners in the majority of cases. A collection of trade leaflets referring to finishes and appliances, perhaps, and some drawings prepared for reading by the initiated, often make up the set. It is highly desirable, especially when a client is commissioning his one and only new building, to provide him with careful guidance on how to use his investment to the best advantage.

As well as clear plans and sections, specially drawn to be easily understood, the client will be assisted if a cut-away axonometric drawing to show service runs is included. There should be a schedule to show the maintenance requirements of the finishes in a coordinated manner.

Record drawings may be used by occupiers who are quite unused to reading technical drawings, and who may have to refer to them in emergency circumstances. Special care should be taken for this reason to provide drawings which can be read easily. The practice of updating the production drawings at the completion of the contract, for the use of the client, is to be frowned on for this reason, since those drawings were prepared for a different purpose and are unlikely to emphasise the points the client will relate to most easily.

For example, the production drawings may be based on a grid of purely imaginary lines which were most useful for setting out and reference purposes, but are irrelevant to the occupier. Drawings which relate to the sizes of rooms and emphasise walls and openings will be more useful to the client.

Design drawings

The main aim of this important set of documents is to convince the client (and perhaps the planning authority or even the public) that the design solution offered is a suitable one from every point of view: to sell the scheme. There is a danger, though, of being so anxious to perform this function that the actual nature of the proposed building is misrepresented. It should be a priority to ensure that design drawings do not mislead, but give a true picture of the proposal. There must be no exaggerated perspective or unrealistic viewpoints: the surroundings should be accurately indicated, and there should be enough detail (cars, trees, people) to a scale the reader can relate to for him to get an accurate idea of the scale of the proposed building.

Colour can appropriately be used on design drawings, so long as this last rule is observed.

Detailed development drawings

As the design proceeds, orthographic drawings are likely to be produced which set out firstly potential solutions to detailed problems, and later the solutions actually adopted. It seems sensible for the first of these drawing types to be produced in pencil and the second in ink, since these will be permanent drawings – and this differentiation will also make clear to all members of the team the nature of the drawing with which they are dealing.

During the development of detailed design, sketches, perspectives, diagrams and axonometric or isometric drawings may help the team understand the implications of the alternative potential solutions between which they are choosing (see below).

The most productive way of building up a set of production drawings is almost always that, after the structural grid and overall size of the building have been established, the smallest details (window sections, for example) referenced to the grid and drawn to full size should be determined. The team can then work downwards in scale while the scope of their drawings increases, through sections at 1:20, to layout drawings at 1:100 and a site plan at 1:500 (or whatever scales best suit the project). In this way, though the windows (to follow through the example initiated above) are shown only diagrammatically to 1:20, there is no danger of the smaller-scale drawing having to be altered later when window details are developed. Similarly, if the 1:20 establishes the relationship of structure to cladding, the sizes of rooms shown to 1:100 will be correct.

The drawings eventually produced in this way are likely to require a minimum of alteration due to later decisions invalidating earlier ones.

Perspective drawings

Although the perspective is a geometric drawing, and actually quite different from what we see (the difference being due to the fact that we see on a spherical 'screen' while a perspective assumes a flat one) yet we have become so accustomed to reading perspectives that this is a suitable type of drawing to use when information about the eventual appearance of a building or its effect on the environment has to be conveyed to the client or to the public. We must remember that lay people find orthographic drawings confusing to translate into a three-dimensional ideas, and the ability to produce accurate perspective drawings – ones which do not falsify spatial effects – is essential if the client is to be kept informed.

For a perspective to be useful in this way it is vital for the viewpoint to have been chosen to show the design from a vantage point that will in the event be available, and also that the viewpoint should be sufficiently far back to minimise the distorting effect of the flat 'screen'. As a rule, if an approximation to realism is wanted, the building should be enclosed within a 30° cone from the viewpoint, and the picture plane should be perpendicular to the centre of that cone. It is also important that use of the height line should be properly understood.

Setting up a perspective

Setting up a geometric perspective is much less difficult than many people appear to believe, provided two points are borne in mind:
1. A perspective projection is a CONVENTION. It does not show an object exactly as it would be seen by the eye, but gives a reasonable approximation to that view IF THE RULES ARE FOLLOWED.
2. The drawing must be systematically carried out.

The construction of a perspective projection depends on the fact that parallel lines appear to converge at a point on the horizon. All perspectives are artificial, because the plane on to which they are projected is flat, whereas the eye perceives a concave field. If, however, a viewpoint sufficiently far back from the object is adopted the distortions will be minimised.

The simplest form of perspective uses only one, central, vanishing point (VP). This system can be used either to give a view into a space from the centre of one side, or to give an 'electric light bulb' view from above, which is a good way of showing an interior.

The steps in setting up a one-point perspective are as follows:
1. The vanishing point VP is marked centrally on the paper, and a horizontal line (eye level, or horizon) drawn through it.
2. The elevation of the distant wall can now be drawn to scale, correctly related to eye level.
3. Lines to mark the ceiling and floor lines of the side walls are drawn through the corners, projecting outwards from VP.
4. At any suitable point, verticals and horizontals are drawn to indicate the near wall.
5. The centre point of the room can be found by drawing-in diagonals on the floor, and any subdivision in the *length* of the space will be obtained in this way, since the distances to be drawn along the side walls will be in geometric progression to represent equal steps.
6. Detail can now be added, taking care that all lines parallel to the depth of the room converge on VP and that all verticals are shown as vertical lines.

It will readily be seen that this procedure would be equally suitable as representation of an exterior view of a street or square, and that it could be adapted to a view from above.

A two-point perspective gives a fuller three-dimensional effect and is appropriate for most exteriors and some interiors.

The steps in setting up a two-point perspective are as follows:

1. Draw plan to scale at a suitable angle, taking into account the details required to be shown.
2. Establish the eye point so that the plan and height lie within a 30° cone of vision. This is vital to minimise distortion if realism is required, though sometimes, for dramatic effect, it may be deliberately ignored.
3. Draw the picture plane on plan. This MUST be perpendicular to the cone of vision, and can be at any distance from the eye depending on the finished drawing size required. Thus, the picture plane may fall behind the plan, between the eye and the plan, or cut through it.
4. Project lines from the eye to the picture plane through all the salient points of the building.
5. Draw lines PARALLEL to the sides of the building from the eye, to intersect the picture plane, and mark vanishing points (VPs) on plan at these intersections.
6. Project one side of the plan to intersect the picture plane, and mark height line (HL) on plan.
7. Moving to clear space reserved at the top of the sheet, draw the horizon.
8. Project VPs, HL and lines representing salient points of building vertically into picture area, to intersect horizon, indicating clearly which is which.
9. Mark a scale of heights on the height line at HL to the same scale as that used to draw the plan.
10. Project the ground and sky lines by using the VPs (on which they will converge) and the height line HL, so that they intersect the verticals.

I realise that even with the diagrams this sounds remarkably complicated, but I can assure my readers that if they will take the trouble to learn to set up a two-point perspective of a simple rectangular form they will discover that by a systematic application of the same process very complicated shapes can be tackled.

Curved forms are dealt with by superimposing a square grid, and plotting points on the curve.

When all the main lines and major details have been plotted in the way described, the construction may, if wished, be used as the basis for a freer sketch, and colour, shadow and tone added.

The setting-up of perspectives is not difficult if it is done systematically, and the ability to produce them rapidly is a most useful skill (Fig. 9.10).

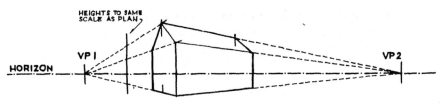

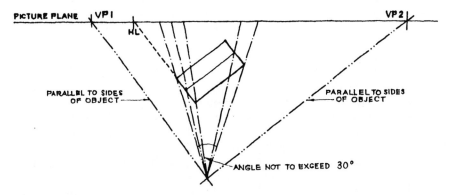

Fig. 9.10 The geometric perspective

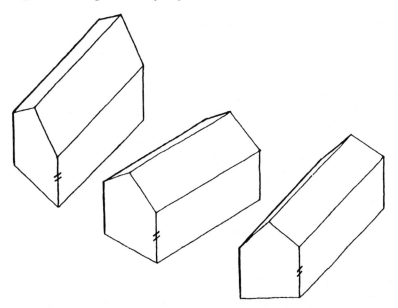

Fig. 9.11 Axonometric, isometric and oblique projections

Axonometric, isometric and oblique projections

Drawings of these kinds are easier to draw than perspectives, but considerably less realistic, and less easy to read. Their place is in communication within the initiated design team, when they can provide three-dimensional information easily. In particular, the axonometric is a straightforward method of providing accurately dimensioned three-dimensional information, and for this reason it can also be a useful way of conveying constructional information to the builder.

Joints and other features of complex geometric shapes may be difficult to follow from conventional orthographic drawings, but immediately clear from an axonometric drawing (Fig. 9.11).

Lettering

There is only one sensible criterion to judge the success of the lettering on a drawing – its legibility. The simplest style which can be produced quickly should be adopted, and gimmicks and personalised features which are thought to add 'style' to the drawing – but do so at the expense of legibility – should be avoided. Stencilled or rub-on lettering is generally time-consuming to do well, so it is best reserved for important presentation drawings, and legible handwriting or printing, provided it is neat and does not distract from the 'meat' of the drawing, is suitable. The drawing of guidelines – indeed proper planning of the placing of all the notes – is really indispensable if the drawing is to serve its purpose of conveying information in the most efficient possible way. There will almost always need to be a hierarchy of weights and sizes of lettering – title, names of main elements, descriptive notes, perhaps, at the simplest. It is important to lay this information out so that each note is clearly seen to relate to the relevant part of the drawing, and no two notes conflict. Repetition should be avoided.

We all face the temptation to show ourselves as industrious by making our drawings look as 'busy' as possible, by putting in every note we can think of. Actually, we should aim to make our drawings look very simple and easy to read. We are trying to tell the reader something important, not to blind him with science (Fig. 9.12).

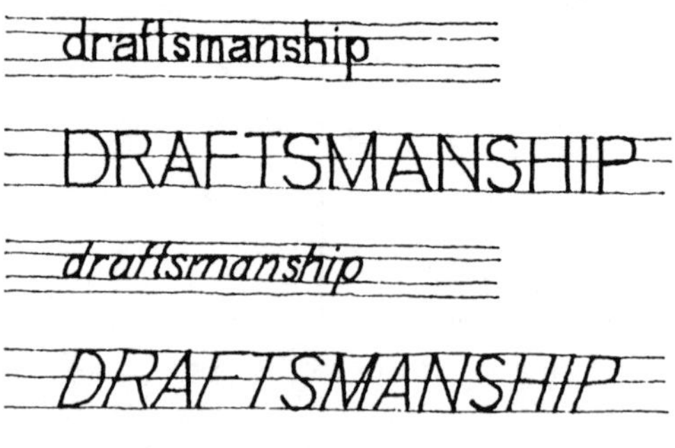

Fig. 9.12 The best lettering is that which is easiest to read

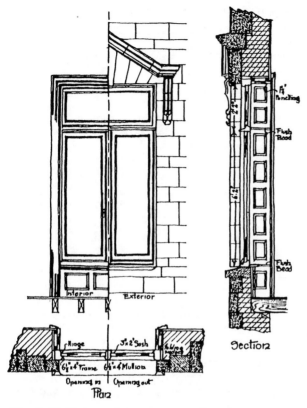

Fig. 9.13 Conventions vary over the years

Drawings generally

It is important that all drawings in a set conform to accepted conventions. Such conventions do vary over the years (as comparison of Figs. 9.13 and 9.14 will show). This must be a convention understood by the expected reader, and if unconventional symbols or unusual reference points are used it may be necessary to include explanatory material in the set of drawings.

Models

The use of meticulous presentation models to convey the effect of a completed project is very common, but can seriously mislead. The charm of a miniature can distort the effect, and the use of a periscope to allow a more realistic viewpoint to be attained has much to recommend it.

Models are, of course, very popular with the public, and to display

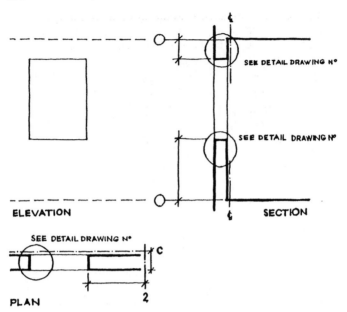

Fig. 9.14 The criterion of a good drawing is how well it conveys its meaning

a professionally made model of a project can often disarm criticism where a favourable public response is important – in the case of a large-scale city centre project, for example, or a building planned for an area of outstanding natural beauty.

It is critical that such models should be realistic in their effect, but there are other models that can usefully be employed during the development of a scheme that can be diagrammatic. From quite early stages in discussion of the massing that may be proposed, to make rapid sketch models can be an effective way of demonstrating the strengths and limitations of potential solutions. Such models can concentrate entirely on the particular point under discussion, ignoring detail or realism, and can therefore be simply made. As the scheme develops, it is, of course, possible to increase the detail added to such a model, and this can be specially appropriate if the design is one of three-dimensional intricacy, such as a concert hall.

Another type of model that is less used in building than it might be is the model detail, whether that displays the detailed layout of furniture and fittings in a hospital ward, or the junction between column, window and cladding. Such models can reveal snags that might not otherwise have been apparent – as well as sometimes showing up quite clearly how a foreseen difficulty can be overcome. These models are usually known as 'mock-ups' if they are done to full-size. If full study of the anthropometrics of the problem is available mock-ups of the arrangement of accommodation may be redundant as design aids, but they may have a use in convincing a client that a solution he believes to be cramped (from drawings) is in fact viable.

Sample panels, provided as a basis for a specification ('equal to the quality of the sample panel provided . . .') hardly come into the category of models, yet clearly perform a useful function as communications. A panel of accepted quality is a far more accurate criterion than any written description or drawing could be. The builder knows precisely, and without argument, what is expected of him, and can therefore price confidently, and there is a clear basis for the settlement of any disputes which may arise.

Written communications

It is as important to the architectural technician that he should have a good command of written English as that he should be able to draw, as many of his communications with others in the design team and with the builder will be in written form. An accurate and discriminating use of language is necessary, but this should avoid pedantry, the endeavour being to be immediately and accurately understood. It is essential to be clear in one's own mind of the message to be communicated, and then to make the simplest possible statement of that material. While courtesy will naturally make relationships easier, clarity ought not to be sacrificed to the desire not to upset the recipient. For example, if a proposal put forward by a colleague seems to be such arrant nonsense that it would be a waste of everyone's time to pursue it, it would be better to say so clearly – perhaps sweetening the pill by referring to the many good ideas that have originated from the same source in the past – than to express 'some concern' at the proposals' viability – which might lead to a good deal of abortive development work.

This is, of course, a simple example from the letters and memoranda that will flow between the members of a design team. There are other communications in written form that need to be considered, many of which are listed below. In every case, the purpose of the composition needs to be considered, so that words are used effectively to convey a precise meaning.

Memoranda

It is advantageous to keep clear records of decisions taken, of points of view to be taken into account and generally of the day-to-day discussions on which design work is based. It is very easy, a year later, to have forgotten the basis for abandonment of a proposal and perhaps to retrace one's steps unnecessarily. It can also be forgotten that a particular action was taken in response to an instruction from elsewhere, if no record is kept. Confirmatory memoranda cover these points, and it is in general desirable that succinct notes should be kept of all telephone and casual conversations, if these might affect one's actions. It is essential that the context of the conversation should be recorded, and this is perhaps best achieved by the old fashioned memorandum book, or failing that by a file kept in strict date order for the purpose.

Typical memorandum confirming an informal discussion.

```
Memo to J Grey, Quantity Surveyors' Office
     from W Brown, Architects Office.
                                   dated     3.5.19-
White's Toy Factory
May I confirm the following points arising from our discussion
yesterday:-

1.  You believe the external cladding is likely to exceed the
    Cost Plan, as detailed.  The cost will have to be compensated
    for by savings, and the most likely source for these is the
    floor.  You will quantify the saving needed, and let me know
    the implications on the design of the upper floors.

2.  By the end of the week I will prepare a sketch detail of the
    proposed perimeter services duct, so that you can cost it and
    it can be discussed at the Design Team meeting next Wednesday.

3.  You hope to have definite costings for the use of the imported
    double glazed windows we discussed, for comparison with the
    purpose made ones being developed, by next Wednesday's meeting
    at the latest.  A decision on this is urgent as the cladding
    cannot be finalised until it is made.
```

Confirmatory letter

Where an action based on instructions received verbally could have far-reaching consequences (a decision not to adopt a particular material, or to employ a particular manufacturer's products, for example) such an instruction should always be confirmed by dated, formal letter. It is always possible for a verbal instruction to be hastily given, without full appreciation of the corollaries, and written confirmation, pointing out any after-effects the decision might have, gives an opportunity for mature consideration. If such a letter passes unanswered, one may consider it confirmed, but otherwise it is foolish to rely on oral instructions alone.

It should be noted that the intention of such confirmatory letters should not be simply to allocate the blame for unconsidered decisions elsewhere (though that may be a side effect!). It is a recognition that opinions expressed 'off the cuff' do not carry the same weight as carefully considered ones.

Typical letter from Architect to Client confirming instructions

Brown, Brown Partners,
Architects,
100 Scarlet Row,
Magentamarket.

Your ref: 999/9
Our ref: BB/m 90/NB/fc.

1st January 19-

Dear Mr White,

TOY FACTORY AT MAGENTAMARKET

I wish to confirm your instruction that dust extraction plant
manufactured by Messrs Dunn and Sons should be used for this
project.

May I confirm that I have explained the desirability of exploring
the industry a little further before coming to a decision. Dunn's
admittedly produce the most compact plant I know of, that will
do the job required, but I am unable to give you any assurances
regarding the reliability of their products, or indeed that they
will remain in business throughout the expected life of the plant -
so that maintenance could become a problem. If it became necessary
later to house less compact plant, this could pose serious problems,
but I understand that you wish to obtain the advantages of the
small scale of Dunn's plant by minimising the scale of the plant
room, and you do not wish any extra space allowance to be made.

I can assure you that your wishes will be carried out.

Yours sincerely

Walter Brown
Partner in Charge.

Messrs White and White,
Toy Manufacturers,
Scarlet Square,
Magentamarket.

For the attention of Mr R White.
cc Miss N Black, Mrs T Blew (Bage and Daughter, Consulting Engineers)

Agenda

Formal meetings are discussed below, but it should be pointed out that
all parties to a meeting benefit if the subjects for discussion are known
in advance. Proper preparation for a meeting can shorten the time
spent in it – and ensure that the time which must be consumed around
tables is used to the best advantage. Agendas should always include
confirmation of the minutes of previous meetings, and the date of the
succeeding one; there should always be an opportunity to speak to
'matters arising' from the previous minutes; and 'any other business'
should always be included, to allow for the discussion of unforeseen
matters. Apart from this, the agenda should make clear exactly what

the purpose of the meeting is, and if important decisions are expected, it is wise to include draft resolutions, so that they may be considered in advance.

Typical agenda for a design team meeting

```
White's Toy Factory.
Please attend a meeting of the design team in the Conference
Room at 10 a.m. on Wednesday 10th May 19-

AGENDA

Apologies for non-attendance.
Minutes of previous meeting.
Matters arising from the minutes.
Reports on Progress:  Architect
                      Structural Engineer
                      Mechanical Engineer
                    . Electrical Engineer
External Cladding and Windows.
Perimeter Service Duct.
Any Other Business.
```

Minutes

There is no need for verbatim minutes to be kept of meetings, but it is essential to record the names of those present and who they represent, as well as apologies for absence received.

The minutes should also cover and set out major decisions reached, and any important points raised in discussion, whether these proved acceptable to the meeting as a whole or not. If any matters were left for subsequent discussion, this should be recorded.

If the meeting was called to monitor progress, the matter of any progress reports, including explanations offered for divergence from an agreed programme will need, too, to be included in the minutes.

Finally, a list should be included of the persons to whom the minutes are to be circulated. As in the case of confirmatory letters, anyone who receives a copy of minutes without challenging them is assumed to have accepted them as a correct record of the meeting.

Typical minutes of design team meeting

```
WHITE'S TOY FACTORY

MINUTES of the Meeting held on Wednesday 10th May 19- at 10 a.m.

PRESENT:     Mr W Brown    Architect (Chair)
             Miss N Black  Assistant Architect
             Mrs J Grey    Quantity Surveyor
             Mr R Gold     Structural Engineer
             Mrs T Blew    Mechanical Engineer
             Mr S Bough    Electrical Engineer
             Mr F Creem    (Minutes)
Apologies for non-attendance were received from Mr M Green, Landscape
Architect.
1.  Minutes.  1.1  The minutes of the previous meeting were taken as
                   read and agreed, subject to the amendment of 3.1
```

to read 'as well as the boiler.' in lieu of 'any old broiler'.

2. Matters arising from the Minutes.

    2.1 There were no matters arising other than those covered by the agenda.

3. Architect's report.

    3.1 Miss Black reported that progress was being maintained in accordance with the agreed programme in general.

    3.2 The non-appearance of the botanical report was delaying preparation of the landscaping plan, but as little other work was dependent upon this, it was unlikely that serious delays would result.

    3.3 A decision on the detail of the external cladding and windows was urgently required to avoid a future delay.

4. Structural Engineer's Report.

    4.1 Mr Gold confirmed that until the cladding had been finalised he was unable to determine the precise sections for the pressed steel frame, and that this was liable to cause a delay.

5. Mechanical Engineer's Report

    5.1 Mrs Blew reported that the bankruptcy of the firm selected by the client (and contrary to her advice) to supply dust extraction plant, would entail considerable reconsideration of the plant layout and space requirements.

    This could have important implications for the plan generally. After discussion it was agreed that the question should be resolved as a matter of urgency. The delay involved should be quantified and reported to the client within a week.

6. Electrical Engineer's Report.

    6.1 Mr Bough reported satisfactory progress.

7. External Cladding and Windows.

    7.1 Mrs Grey tabled a cost comparison between purpose designed windows and ready made double glazed. After discussion it was agreed to approve the former on the grounds of appearance, since though dearer they could be provided within the Cost Plan.

    7.2 Figures were produced by the Quantity Surveyor to show that the additional cost of the external cladding detail preferred at the previous meeting could be met by a saving of 3 per cent on flooring. This could be obtained by including granolithic rather than terrazzo to stores. The client had no objection to this, in view of the improved standard of thermal insulation expected from the revised cladding, and the change was approved.

8. Perimeter Service Duct.

    8.1 Miss Black produced sketch details of the proposed perimeter service duct, which were closely examined and approved for further development.

9. Any Other Business.

    9.1 Mrs Blew produced drawings to show the

functional requirements of the tank room.
It was seen that as arranged the tank room
would be unduly obtrusive, and Miss Black and
Mrs Blew agreed to meet, so as to produce
revised proposals for the next meeting.

10. Next Meeting.

    10.1 The next meeting will be held on Wednesday
7th June at 10 a.m. at the Architect's office.

    10.2 Since decisions on site layout would be
required, Mr Green was to be asked to make a
special effort to attend.

11. Distribution All present.

    Mr M Green, Landscape Architect.

    File.

Specifications

The object of a specification is to set out as accurately as possible
exactly what is required as far as quality is concerned in a particular
item. Although there is a great deal of jargon used (one suspects
sometimes almost for its own sake, and without full understanding of
what is being said!) in writing specifications, much of this is
unnecessary. One's interest is to ensure that the item as supplied is
precisely what is required, and that the price paid is appropriate. This
can be done by reference to a British Standard Specification, by
scheduling performance criteria – or even by quoting the product of a
particular manufacturer as providing an acceptable standard! The
method adopted, of course, depends entirely on the item being
described and the degree to which quality is critical, and I do not wish
to trespass into the territory of the many excellent books on the
subject. I should, however, draw attention to the importance, in
preparing a specification as in any other kind of communication, of
defining the objectives of the document, and the ways in which it will
be interpreted – and by whom – before any attempt to compose the
wording.

Bills of quantities

Architectural technicians are likely to be concerned with bills of
quantities as interpreters more often than as originators. They should
be aware that the bill means precisely what it says – that this has been
composed as carefully as their specification or the notes on their
drawings, and that phrases have not been casually included or omitted.

Contract

The contract, even more than the bill of quantities, is likely to be the
subject of legalistic interpretation, and indeed every clause of the
standard forms has had its interpretation rigorously tested in the
courts. There should be no room for argument if the standard forms
are adhered to – excepting that there will always be room for a dispute
where two parties enter into an agreement, because they will always

each put his own gloss on the phrases involved! If there can be disputes about forms as well tested as these, this indicates the danger of entering on to building work without a formal contract, or with some form of agreement in a letter, with a few phrases and a lot of optimism. Alterations to contracts are dangerous – do-it-yourself ones even more so (see Ch. 13).

Architect's instructions

Because architect's instructions have a defined place under the contract, they deserve to be written as carefully as the bills of quantities they vary. They should always indicate what alteration is being made, or what provisional sum is being spent, for example, and what the total effect of the instruction is on the contract sum.

Personal meetings

Formal meetings

It is undeniable that a great deal of the time spent in formal meetings at any stage of a project is unproductive, and yet the formal progress meeting can be among the most effective channels of communication available to any team. It is one occasion when all the parties will be brought together, they will be set specific aims and asked to account for any failure to meet them, and potential difficulties can frequently be foreseen and avoided.

The success of such meetings depends to a large extent on the skill of the chairman. He must prepare (in conjunction with the secretary or notetaker) an agenda (see above) which allows for the discussion of every relevant topic, and he must then ensure that everyone has an opportunity to speak on each topic, but that the discussion remains relevant and productive.

Skill in chairing a meeting is very largely a matter of being well prepared: of knowing what points are likely to be raised, and (if two antithetical points of view are likely to be voiced) understanding the reasoning behind each side of the case and allowing an equal opportunity for the development of each. Once a point has been made, the chairman should not allow undue repetition – and eventually he must ensure that a decision is reached. Because in the end it is the architect who has to reach a decision and ensure that it is followed, if a consensus cannot be reached, and it is very often the architect who takes the chair at progress meetings, his position can be difficult. It is hard to listen objectively to divergent, points of view, knowing that in the end one can insist that one's own viewpoint should prevail. This is one reason for the formal procedure of such meetings, which helps to distance the chairman somewhat from the discussion, and the formalities of always addressing the chair, of speaking only to the agenda, and of accepting decisions once reached should quite strictly be adhered to.

Informal meetings

If any team is to work successfully together, regular informal meetings are of course essential. The members of the team need to be on friendly terms – but they must not forget that they have a formalised relationship as colleagues. Professional views expressed within the team are no less binding than if they were given on a more formal occasion – and the confirmation of oral statements (see above) remains desirable.

The geographical arrangement in which the team finds itself can be influential on its interaction. 'Bureaulandschaft' offices – ones organically laid out so that everyone is closest to the colleagues with whom he works most – are supposed to simplify teamwork. On the other hand, some firms would say that this proximity reduces the respect of one group for another. A firm of architects has been heard to say that they worked best with consultants based in another town, because one listens more carefully to a comparative stranger.

It should be realised that mutual respect between colleagues is more important to the success of the team than liking, and that such respect can be expressed by taking the trouble to explain oneself fully as much as by listening carefully to the other party.

Chapter 10

Storage and retrieval of information

The need for storage and easy retrieval

No one can carry in his head all the facts he needs to complete the tasks allotted to him. Indeed, anyone who pretends to such encyclopedic knowledge is either limiting his view of the world to a very narrow range or else using mental capacity that would be better occupied in utilising and evaluating information stored elsewhere. This is a major difference between computers and people: the former are marvellous at storing any information fed into them, and recalling it on demand, but can only use it in simple ways that have been laboriously taught. They are very quick, of course, in doing this – but they're not clever. People are excellent at noting nuances and overtones, responding to relationships and thinking – but slower: they also have much poorer memories.

Anyone who has attempted to rely on memory knows how deceptive it can be. We fail (whatever mnemonics we adopt) to recall the whole of the material, we may recall part of it in an adapted form that results from our earlier use of it, and quite simple misunderstandings can be perpetuated. We remember best the knowledge we use most frequently – it's easier to remember your friend's telephone number than your own – and once our mind moves into well worn tracks it's hard to change direction. To rely on memory in the building field is only possible if we are content to limit ourselves to a very small range of well tried options, whether from the design or from the constructional point of view.

The scope of human memory is narrow, though it can be trained, and we can only be confident in familiar mental paths which have been retrodden on many occasions. There is an ever present danger that the person who prides himself on his excellent memory is one who is reluctant to innovate.

One reason for the widespread adoption of continuous assessment in place of formal examinations in recent years has been the feeling that the latter are more likely to test memory, whereas the real-life situation students will eventually have to face will be concerned less with recall than with the use made of information.

On the other hand, looking things up takes time, and time is often our scarcest resource. If material is stored in a disordered fashion, no one will bother to search for the fact he needs. He will either guess (which could be disastrous) or else go back to the originator of the material (which is inefficient).

Printed material

Books and trade literature

It must be a familiar syndrome that an individual has a few basic reference books (some of which were his college textbooks, and may by now be outdated) by his desk. Not all will be present – some will be at home, where he has been working on a private problem, and some may have been lent to colleagues, though he's not quite sure to whom. He also has a varied pile of trade literature sent in fairly recently by representatives who happen to have his name, and more that he wrote for specially, in connection with a job that was finished a year or two ago. Other people in the office have similarly heterogeneous collections, which they don't mind lending (Fig. 10.1).

This situation, though we can muddle along with it for a while, raises two questions:

1. *Can we rely on the information we find being comprehensive?*
   Clearly not. Even if we find three window-manufacturers' catalogues, and are prepared to accept one of them as suitable to our purpose, we can never be sure that there may not be another that might be even more useful about somewhere, if only we could put our hand on it. This is a very inefficient way of storing even the limited range of facts we have.

2. *Is the material accurate?*
   Even if firms have kept us on their regular mailing list, how can we be sure the leaflet we have is the latest that has been published? Obviously we have no way of knowing this at all.

There are, then, three objectives for the storage of information:

1. It must be quick to refer to, otherwise no one will use it. Ideally,

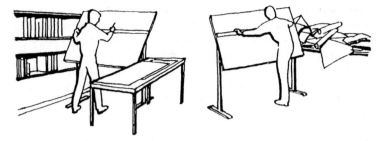

Fig. 10.1 All the information in the world is useless if you can't find it when you want it

the reader should not need to leave his desk. Until electronic communications become the norm, or offices can afford expensive and elaborate document handling machinery like the 'conservatrieve' system which brings up documents from a remote store at the touch of a keyboard, this will continue to be necessary.

One should, however, know how to find the information and be able either to go direct to it or call it up easily and rapidly. All related information should be kept together, so that one can follow up a line of enquiry without inconvenience, and browsing and reference to a number of materials at one time should be possible. If only one item can be consulted at once, a valuable service is lost. Comparisons are often vital, between different documents.

2. It must be as comprehensive as it can be made, within clearly defined and understood limits, so that users can be confident that nothing relevant is being overlooked because it is absent. This may have the corollary that material cannot be taken away from the store, or else that a very clear record is kept as to the whereabouts of each document – and someone chases up those not returned promptly.

We ought never to feel the need to write to a research or commercial organisation to make sure they have nothing more up-to-date than the papers we have before us.

A difficulty is in defining what may become relevant in some set of circumstances that have yet to arise. Usually it is necessary to limit the topics which will be covered in detail to those in everyday use, but to cover those fully. The attempt to be truly comprehensive is doomed to failure except in the very largest organisations, and even there can lead to a collection so unwieldy as to deter users. New topics can always be added as it becomes clear they are needed.

3. It must be up to date.

This involves pruning dead wood as well as adding new

material. If out-of-date material is retained this has the effect both of potentially misleading the reader and of making the information centre difficult to consult. There is no value in padding – the collection should be as small as possible. If there are good historical reasons for retaining out-of-date literature (as might be the case in a practice which did a great deal of conservation or alteration work) an archive should be established as a separate system.

These conditions can be met, expensively, by feeding all available facts into a computer, for instant recall. While at present this is a prohibitive system for most organisations, the development of the use of computer-linked video displays, such as that being developed in connection with the Telecom organisation, or of Teletext, which uses ordinary TV receivers (suitably modified) to tap into a store of available knowledge which can be constantly updated, may change this situation. Once such a system became widespread, manufacturers, advisory bodies and research institutions could feed-in constantly revised material which would immediately become available to every subscriber. It will of course be seen that the value of this would be directly related to its comprehensiveness. It seems that the balance between the cost and the usefulness of such systems is likely to move in favour of their adoption. We may see the cathode-ray tube taking the place of the office bookshelf, but without extensive experience of use it is impossible to say how effective this might be or how likely its widespread adoption.

Simpler systematic methods are in use at present, and seem serviceable. Simplicity is the key, otherwise the system will just not be used. While a method that produces material for the reader at the touch of a key can be intrinsically complicated so long as it is easy to use, a system where the reader is to have access to the whole body of material must be very straightforward indeed in layout, access and documentation. Complicated classification systems devised by individuals for specific applications have their charm, and are usually easily followed by their authors – and impossible to use by anyone else. Rather than make the effort of understanding such a leviathan, the newcomer abandons it and either adopts a system of his own or goes back to the situation described at the beginning of this chapter.

Simplicity is aided by standardisation. The more widely a classification is adopted the better it will be understood. There is, therefore, a good case for subjugating our individual preferences in this respect to an overall, generally adopted norm.

Apart from anything else, if one should be run over and rushed to hospital a hastily recruited deputy would find our work easy to take over.

The 'Library' will generally run most efficiently if it is overseen by a single individual. Such a person would be responsible for obtaining, referencing and discarding material. He should not, however, allow himself to become the office wiseacre, the answerer of all queries. He is not to be expected to have total familiarity with every document in his care. He may well think it right, however, to bring new material to the attention of those he thinks may be interested, and he may be a valuable guide to the contents of the collection.

Each individual should have unfettered access to the collection, though (due to the frailty of us all) it may be necessary to record loans and keep watch for unauthorised borrowing. Such open access implies that material must be shelved in classification order, so that individuals can understand and use the collection easily. The kind of system that depends on shelving by size and in effect extending the shelves at one end as material arrives (which operates in many old-established libraries) involves searching catalogues for shelfmarks and is unsuitably cumbersome.

Reference will often be to areas of knowledge rather than to single documents that are known to exist in advance. The reader will need to browse to discover the parameters of a particular choice or what components may be on the market. This cannot be done unless all relevant material is shelved contiguously.

It is important that reshelving should be done by the information officer, otherwise mistakes are inevitable. Mistakes tend to invalidate the system, as well as being thoroughly irritating. The main advantage of a well-run information library should be its reliability.

If the classification system adopted for use in arranging trade literature can be adapted also for use with documents originated within the office, this will clearly provide a single comprehensive pattern into which any material of any kind either to be stored or to be recalled will fit.

Provided the overall shape of such a classification is once memorised there should be considerable advantages in use.

Besides books and trade literature, other material which requires to be classified for easy recall includes letters, specification clauses, elements in bills of quantities, samples, and, of course, drawings of many different kinds and at a variety of scales. If a system can be devised which will allow inclusion of these items as well as printed material, this would have evident advantages. For example, if books on daylighting, window manufacturers' catalogues, window details and specification notes, and indeed sample window sections, all bore a similar code this would appear logical, be easy to remember and easier to use, and mistakes would immediately be apparent. This would not be the case if a series of different codings were used for the different categories of information. Each category, however, presents its own difficulties, and these can be hard to resolve.

Books, trade literature and magazine articles may come in a variety of formats, though the A4 page-size is increasingly being adopted. Magazines usually have to be dismembered if all their parts can be stored logically, so a good deal of the material is thin and floppy. If this is kept in loose-leaf files, inserting new material and removing old can be time consuming, and the acess to a considerable body of literature on a topic may mean a good deal else has to be laboriously moved. On the other hand, if such material is stored in boxes or trays at can be difficult to consult, and easily misplaced.

Any boxes or files used need to be clearly titled so that the contents can be ascertained without the need to remove them from the shelves.

Books and files need to be available together, separate sequences being difficult both to use and to keep up.

Standard specification clauses

The use of standard specification clauses can be a safeguard against omissions, provided they are used as a quarry and not a crutch. Standard clauses should never be copied blindly, but may refresh the mind and stimulate thought on what is actually required.

It may well be appropriate to store copies of such clauses along with the printed material referred to above, and if this is to be done the classifications obviously have to be congruent.

Most offices will wish, however, also to store copies in a sequence of their own where they are immediately available in much the order in which they would be used in an actual specification. This may usefully be a card index.

It will be useful if the classification adopted allows detail and specification for a particular element to be identified easily. A similar classification may be applied to bill items for ease of reference, and this can be done whether or not elemental bills are used, though it is simpler where this is so.

Drawings

When beginning to consider the way in which drawings are to be classified and stored, it immediately becomes apparent that every drawing in fact belongs to two separate and distinct sequences. Firstly, it is one of a set of drawings prepared for a particular job, and needs to be accessible to everyone concerned with that job, and secondly a window detail (say) is part of a series of window drawings which have been prepared for different jobs over the years. It is possible that some such details may be found so successful that they become standard details of the office, and available for use on other jobs. Some details (and particularly in the case of system building, of course) will be deliberately prepared as standard details, to become part of the vocabulary of design.

No drawing should bear two different classifications, but the number it bears must indicate its natural place in each of these sequences.

The classification number will not of course stand alone. However

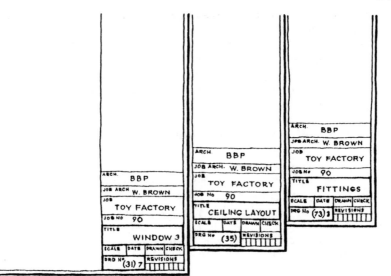

Fig. 10.2 It is essential that everyone understands the system

carefully the drawing is identified by code, it must still bear title of job and of office, title of drawing, scale and date.

Unless the sizes of drawing sheets are limited in variety, difficulties in storage are to be expected. There is much merit in establishing a standard sheet size for each of the categories (layout, detail and full size), and insisting on these being used.

A4 is a convenient size for many details.

One question to be asked is whether revision of a drawing generates a new number, or whether the existing number is just raised to another revision level (e.g. . . . (R3)). If the negative has been altered, so that no original negative can be identified, it is suggested that a revision suffix should be used, whereas redrawing should generate a fresh number.

Simplicity will in any case be aided if numbers of drawings required are allocated in advance. In the old-fashioned system, each drawing prepared was given the next available number, so that window details (to take one example) could have numbers bearing no evident relationship to one another. They would be difficult to identify and to find physically. In the system advocated, all window details as well as schedules related to them would lie together in the sequence no matter in what order they were prepared.

The convenience of the user on site is a high priority in arranging the set of drawings, and any sequence which separates drawings elementally is therefore advantageous. Open-ended branches to the numbering system will be necessary, exactly as they are for the filing of

trade literature or books, so that interpolations can be made without
upsetting the classification of subsequent material.

Bill of quantities

The referencing of bills by a system in agreement to the classification
of other material will be convenient for everyone using them, if it can
be arranged.

Letters and other written communications

Traditionally, written communications are filed in date order. This is
easy and unlikely to result in misfiling when the placing of documents
takes place, but can make it exceedingly difficult to find individual
items, and especially to trace a 'story' through the files. There is no
point in keeping material unless it is going to be easily recalled, and so
the convenience of the filing clerk should give way to the convenience
of the person needing to refer to the files.

If material is broken down too sharply, multiple copies of some
documents may be required, unless everyone concerned with the job
can be persuaded to deal with one topic only in each letter! The system
that appears in practice to work satisfactorily is a more limited
breakdown, so that sequences of letters in date order are filed under
headings of (say) Client, Contractor, Consultants, and Trade
Enquiries, with separate files containing additional copies only of
architects' instructions and minutes of meetings.

In the case of complicated jobs, it may be desirable to break the
sequence down further, allocating separate files to each consultant and
main subcontractor, for example.

The responsibility for determining on to which file a document
should be placed must be known to fall to one individual, otherwise
differences of interpretation will arise, leading to as much (if not
more) difficulty in tracing information as in the case of a single date
sequence.

One thing which should be avoided at all costs is any need for
material once filed ever to be removed from the file. Such a procedure
inevitably results in missing letters.

The system which is most likely to suit all of these categories will
be one into which additional subsections can be interpolated at any
point, and from which open-ended branches can be extended.

Dewey

The Dewey decimal system, which is the basis of most library
classifications in this country, provides just such a basis. Large topic
areas are allocated areas in the sequence of whole numbers, and
increasingly detailed identification can be made by adding decimal
places.

For example, the area 600–699 is allocated to applied sciences and technology, and within this area, 690 – is allocated to building. 700–799 belongs to the Arts, and at 720 includes architecture.

A feature of Dewey which is not always appreciated is that there is a degree of cross-referencing in the decimal figures. The suffix .3 implies a dictionary or encyclopedia, so that a dictionary of building would be found under 690.3, and an encyclopedia of architecture under 720.3. Similarly, the suffix .9 is reserved for histories, so that a history of architecture falls into 720.9 and a history of building into 690.9. A history of a particular type of building or of a special building element would have an additional figure after the .9.

Universal Decimal Classification

UDC is a development from Dewey, and is very complicated to anyone but a librarian.

SfB

These cryptic initials stand, in fact, for the Swedish 'Samarbets kommitten für Byggnadsfragor' but are commonly recognised as the title of the classification system now widely adopted throughout the building industry. This was introduced in a deliberate attempt to provide the kind of framework described. The *Construction Indexing Manual* assists by giving every item an appropriate code number – but

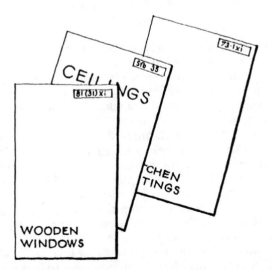

Fig. 10.3 A storage system should be designed as a retrieval system

this is a complicated job, and no attempt at classification should be made unless the manual is to hand. The system now adopted is a refinement on that originally introduced and the correct title is CI/SfB.

Most trade literature, articles and so on these days already bear the appropriate code, and filing in sequence should be relatively simple.

The system has four 'facets' or separate classification tables, and one files under the first of these shown and subsequently under each of the later facets in turn – not all of them are always used. They refer to separate characteristics of the information concerned.

Table 0 Built environment *Numbers without brackets*	Building types, e.g. 6 Religious buildings 66 Monasteries, convents
Table 1 Elements *Numbers with brackets*	Parts or components of a building, e.g. (4) Applied finishes (44) Stair finishes
Table 2/3 Construction form *Letters without brackets*	Capital represents construction form, lower case represents material, e.g. Fi Wood blocks Fg Bricks
Table 4 Activities and requirements *Letters with brackets*	e.g. A Administration A7 Quality control S Durability

As can be seen, any category in all four facets is open-ended, so that the system is capable of virtually infinite extension.

It will also be clear that this classification can be applied to any of the types of material we have been considering. The reference 81(31) Xi will refer to wooden windows for domestic buildings both a trade catalogue and a detail. It is, however, usual to simplify the classifications given to drawings and specification clauses, so that all window details will have (31) as part of their nomenclature. Thus, if the job number was 192, and this was window drawing number 7 of the set for the building, the drawing would be number 192(31)7. If that drawing was subsequently revised, the suffix R1 would be added. Where revisions are referenced, it is common practice to commence revision numbers only after issue of the initial drawings to the builder, so that the first drawing he receives never bears a revision mark.

It will be possible to find all the window drawings for that job easily, since they will be filed in series. It will also be simple to find the window details for any other job, since all will include (31) in their classification.

Libraries

Application of the rules outlined will make the office system of classification simple to apply and to use. It is therefore likely in fact to be fully used. Even the largest office library must inevitably have limitations. While it can and will pursue particular topics and interests to a much greater depth than any individual public library is likely to do, it is important to recognise and use the excellent loan service available through public libraries. These, and the libraries of academic and research institutions, are linked through an Interloan system, so that virtually any published material is rapidly available. Even great public libraries cannot be exhaustive in their stocks, but by agreement each specialises in particular areas, so that in every region every recent book published in Britain is stocked. Libraries belonging to the scheme send details of their acquisitions to a central bureau. The reader is not limited to the stock of his own library, but can draw on regional and national resources.

Additionally, it is worth noting that the British Architectural Library at the RIBA publishes an easily read quarterly list of relevant magazine articles published worldwide, and armed with this information it is possible through the British Lending Library for Science and Technology to obtain a photocopy of any material. This library keeps copies of most technical and scientific periodicals.

Your local librarian will be able to help you to find other and more specialised abstracts and indices – and also to tell you which libraries in your area specialise in the materials most likely to interest you.

A list of these and other sources of useful data is appended, but this is in no way exhaustive.

Your local Public Library (see phone book).

The Library of your local University or Polytechnic, especially if there is a Department of Architecture or Building (see phone book).

The British Architectural Library, RIBA, 66 Portland Place, London W1N 4AD.

The British Lending Library, Boston Spa, Wetherby, West Yorkshire LS23 7BQ.

BSI Library, 2 Park Street, London W1A 2BS.

DOE Headquarters Library, 2 Marsham Street, London SW1P 3EB.

Building centres: the London centre is at 26 Store Street, London WC1E7BT.

Building Research Establishment, Garston, Watford, Herts WD2 7JR.

Agreement Board, P.O. Box 195, Garston, Watford, Herts WD2 7NG.

The following directories, which should be available in your local library, assist in locating obscure information:·

ASLIB Directory – a general guide to sources of information in Great Britain and Ireland.
Whitaker's *Almanack*, which contains vital names and addresses.
'Sources of Information' which is part of the RIBA *Handbook of Architectural Practice and Management.*
Keys to Published Technical and Management Information (RIBA).
British National Bibliography.

Your librarian will be able to introduce you to further more specialised abstracts and indices.

Chapter 11

Design guides and manufacturers' literature

An objective approach to the use of published information

As we have seen, a very large body of published information is at the designer's disposal. He can be in danger of misusing it unless he understands clearly what its limitations are.

Firstly, he should not expect to find complete answers to his particular questions: he may obtain considerable help, advice and guidance, and a good deal of background on how similar problems have been dealt with in the past and may be solved in the future, but he has to remember that his particular problem is unique and that it is his responsibility to come up with the answer to the individual set of circumstances that confront him.

Secondly, material can only be used intelligently and to the best advantage if one understands the aims and objectives of those who wrote and published it. It is essential, therefore, to ask onself from time to time a number of questions regarding the literature one is using:

What do I want from it?　Am I looking for facts, expert opinions, or advice? Is this the best available source?

Why was this document prepared?　Is it an aid to selling, a research paper, a digest of alternatives or a mandatory requirement? What qualifications does the author have for giving me the information in question?

When was it written? Is it up-to-date? Is it comprehensive? Where
can I find matter that might be missing?
For whom was it written? Does the writing presuppose technical
knowledge beyond my scope? Is it intended as a simple
introduction to the subject for non-specialists?

Such an objective approach will avoid the worst pitfalls of taking
everything as of equal importance, providing it is well presented.
Advertising matter, in particular, often pretends to the status of a
scientific paper, and can be misleading.

Sources of information

The advertisement

The copywriter for an advertising agency is interested in keeping the
account – and therefore his copy must demonstrably increase sales or
upgrade his client's image. Naturally he will not include direct
falsehood or misleading statements if he is a responsible man (in any
case, to do so would in the end be counterproductive) but it is good
salesmanship to select one from a miriad facts and present it as
attractively as possible.

The advertisement is meant to catch one's attention, make one
aware of the firm – perhaps, because that is the name one comes across
most frequently in its particular field, make one believe erroneously
that it is the brand leader. The end result should be that one is
predisposed in the firm's favour, and writes off for their brochures and
invites the representative to call.

No one should expect the content of an advertisement to do more
than this: we don't, however, always appreciate the extent to which
our perceptions of the places individual firms have in the industry can
be affected by advertising. Look through the advertisement pages of an
edition or two of the technical press.

Trade leaflets

Trade leaflets sent out to a large mailing list have a very similar
function to that of magazine advertisements. In this I include those
publications which are sent out free and include advertisements for a
very large number of firms, as well as the single-sheet papers which
arrive through one's letterbox. In either case the intention is to raise
awareness of the firm, and to trigger enquiries for more detailed
information.

Trade literature

More detailed brochures and catalogues generally only arrive in
response to a particular request, and they are likely to be far more
informative: materials, sizes and performance as well as potential

Fig. 11.1 Getting the facts right matters more than glossy presentation

applications should be covered. The aim, however, is still to improve sales. Now however, one is being told how to install and use the product. After all, misuse would damage the reputation of the firm.

Instructions which come WITH the product, after the irrevocable order has been placed may be even informative, and may reveal hitherto unsuspected snags.

Trade literature ought to give data which is directly comparable with what is available regarding competing products, but this is not always the case. Comparisons, to be meaningful, frequently involve the conversion of units and considerable calculation if an informed decision is to be made. Reference to the requirements of British Standards Institution or the Building Regulations, where these are applicable, is clearly desirable.

Do note that, once you are on a firm's mailing list, there is not likely to be any difficulty in keeping up-to-date with their literature. The problem is more often in getting off a mailing list, once on it!

The representative
However technically qualified, the representative may be paid at least in part by results: as a commission of orders taken. He should, of course, have sufficient technical background to be able to answer your cogent questions, and must certainly be equipped with a detailed knowledge of the scope and limitations of the product he sponsors. His real expertise, however, is in marketing. I would not for one moment suggest that the representatives of any reputable firm would resort to pressure tactics to induce you to order their products, but nonetheless

we must recognise that the representatives and the firms exist by getting orders at the expense of their rivals. If they do this by producing a better product there is no reason why they should not bring that fact forcefully to our attention.

The representative should be able to give you the absolutely up-to-date situation regarding cost and availability. He should also be ready to come on-site to ensure that his products are being used correctly and to sort out any snags that arise.

Getting to know the representative of the firms you find reliable is well worth while: they will keep you up-to-date with developments of new products, but you have to bear in mind that, however friendly, they are actually looking for orders. They are not likely to tell you if a competitor's product would actually suit your needs more than theirs. Why should they?

Trade organisations

The promotional organisations for particular materials or facets of the industry have an important service to offer. They can present the products of a multitude of small firms who could not individually manage similar coverage, and present comparative data.

Though they are in competition with other materials and so on, they generally have considerable research facilities, and the information they provide has a sound factual basis. They can present an overall picture of all that is on offer in their field as a basis for early choices.

These bodies are, however, still in the business of selling. If a different material would in fact be the most suitable answer to your problem, you may not find that they point this out.

Compendia

Compendia in book form, such as *Specification* or the *Architects Standard Catalogue*, or in the form of an ever updated collection of literature, such as the *Barbour Index*, have obvious attractions as works of reference.

The books, of course, take time to produce, and so must always be treated with caution because such material rapidly becomes outdated. Either type of publication may depend on firms choosing to be included. This can mean both that they are less than comprehensive, and that actual market leaders may decide that they do not need the additional coverage offered by a large entry while up-and-coming newcomers decide to splash out – this clearly leads to a distorted picture of what the industry can actually offer.

In the case of catalogue maintenance systems, material is kept well up-to-date, and the small office which subscribes is actually buying the services of a meticulous librarian to keep its information system serviced.

The information can include both design and constructional data, and may be presented either in reprinted form, as original literature or as microfiche. The disadvantage of the latter is the difficulty of consulting more than one document at once.

Research bodies

The Building Research Establishment issues regular bulletins and digests describing research in hand and conclusions reached. These are authoritative, but of course only refer to the problems investigated, and cannot be regarded as encyclopedic.

The research organisations which are concerned with particular aspects of the industry, such as fire resistance, can generally provide deep and wide-ranging information, which is very authoritative in their particular sphere, and covers every kind of application. Their literature is likely to be based on the assumption, however, that you share their assurance of the overriding priority to be accorded to the concerns with which they are always involved, which may not be the case.

The technical press

Naturally enough, technical journalists like any others have a nose for a good story, and one might expect a tendency to sensationalism. We are, though, lucky enough to have a very responsible technical press, which regards the provision of information in as objective and comprehensive a form as possible as a duty. One naturally has to be able to separate factual reporting from editorial comment, and readers should aim to familiarise themselves with any editorial 'slant' that might colour the piece.

Self-evidently, the technical press is the pre-eminent place to seek really up-to-date news of developments – new ideas, failures, judgements. The space available to describe these may be limited so that one has to look elsewhere for detail.

Government publications

It is very important when relying on information from government sources to distinguish between mandatory requirements and advisory guidelines. Clearly, if a rule is laid down in the Building Regulations, there is no getting away from its demands. A design bulletin of DOE, on the other hand, is another matter. This can be used as a basis for design over a wide field: are there occasions when government approval actually depends on adherence to its precepts?

Such bulletins are based on large collections of factual material and on the collation of wide experience that would otherwise be unavailable, and they therefore provide invaluable background data. They can tend, however, not to be kept up-to-date particularly well, so one should have regard to the date of publication and be prepared to modify one's response in the light of known developments since that time. For example, data on school design might be based on out-of-date criteria as to class size, but be otherwise reliable, or guidance on the layout of estates might be predicated on out-of-date figures for the penetration of car ownership. In either case, slavish following of patterns provided might lead to thoroughly unsatisfactory results.

Planning authority design guides

The preparation of manuals by planning authorities, intended to help intending applicants by demonstrating work which would or would not be acceptable is intended to be nothing but helpful. After all, many applicants in the past have expressed surprise and dismay at having schemes turned down when they could not understand what objection there could be to their proposals. Prior guidance is clearly needed.

One danger, however, can be that the impression may be gained by applicants – and in extreme cases even promulgated by officers – that only work which follows the patterns laid down can be assured of approval, and innovation is discouraged. No one should be deterred from making proposals which abide by the spirit of the overall plan if they contravene the guide in detail (or even in direct opposition to the guide provided a good case can be defended). They are wise, though, to take the trouble to discuss possibly controversial proposals in advance, and listen to opposing points of view.

The secret of making effective use of all kinds of prepared information, wherever it originates, is first to determine exactly what information one requires and seek it out, refusing to be led down irrelevant side-tracks. In this way, you can obtain window sizes without being over impressed by the exaggerated claims on durability also included in the leaflet, or extract anthropometric data from a DOE guide without copying the anachronistic plans illustrated alongside it.

Above all, one must recognise that differences in motivation between originator and user could lead to misunderstanding. Appropriate reservations have to be made.

The understanding of the theory of communication referred to in Chapter 9 is as important to you as a reader as it is in your capacity as an originator of communications.

Chapter 12

Cost constraints

It is a duty for the design team that they should comply with the cost constraints imposed by the client. They will not, of course, accept unreasonable limitations, but the realistic sum the client is willing and able to spend will have been one of the earliest subjects for discussion with him, and if he were making impossible demands this would have been identified and the conditions of the problem changed in one way or another so that the project was seen to be financially viable.

We all recognise, I think, that there is a temptation for the designer to produce what the client says he wants, or what he evidently needs, while letting costs take care of themselves. I have heard a responsible architect argue cogently that this is really what clients want: they are looking for quality, and provided they see that that is what they are offered the money will be found. If this was ever true, I doubt whether it is today. The client quite often has no means whatsoever of raising more money than originally stated, whether it is from government sources, private means, or loan. Money is expensive these days. What clients want, I believe, is to see that they get value for their expenditure, but they expect responsible advisers to use their money wisely and respect the limits they are given.

If the design team do not take sufficient notice of such limits, and operate specifically designed techniques to ensure that they stay within them, they may find themselves with a great deal of work completed on a project, tenders obtained – and the need to cut a substantial percentage of the expenditure. How can this be done? At this stage the most important expenditure (on the structure) is virtually

204

unchangeable: the choice is frequently between omitting a part of the building altogether and making severe cuts to the services and finishes. These, as the most accessible features for cutting, are naturally the most vulnerable. They are also the least likely to provide worthwhile savings. In neither case will the client feel he has been given value for money.

It must be recognised that the need for unexpected savings can arise on even well controlled jobs, if there are unexpected changes in the economic climate, or particularly if a sudden flow of work makes contractors unexpectedly less anxious to tender.

In either event, a sadder and wiser design team may find that sufficient money can only be saved by such severe alterations that redesign is essential. During the inevitable delay the cost of building may well increase again, and the client may not welcome the need to pay a second lot of fees! The doomed-to-failure attempt to make the savings on doorknobs, and the expense of redesign on more modest lines are neither likely to be wholly satisfactory.

If there is any way to avoid such a situation, clearly this should be adopted. Costs should be continuously monitored throughout design (which includes detailing). The cost analysis, on which a cost plan, or budget for the job is based, is a sophisticated tool for this purpose.

Cost analyses

For some years, cost analyses of completed buildings, based on the definition of standard 'elements' of the building rather than trades or components (that is to say, elements such as 'roof' or external wall, rather than trades such as 'carpenter' or 'bricklayer') have been published regularly. From these it is possible to see what the expensive parts of a particular building were, and also by comparing several similar buildings to estimate the proportion of the expenditure on a new building which should go on each element.

The analyses are generally accompanied by sufficient information about the nature of the building, site conditions and the form of contract to indicate any unusual conditions which may have obtained. The Building Cost Information Service (BCIS) which is a subsidiary of the Royal Institution of Chartered Surveyors (RICS), gives two tables, one of which shows preliminaries as a separate item while the other has them distributed between the other elements. This service is easy to use since similar buildings are grouped together.

The *Architects' Journal*, as part of its description of completed buildings, also published cost analyses, but these are hard to find unless they are deliberately filed for the purpose. They have the advantage, however, that as well as total cost and cost per square metre for each element, they express costs as a percentage of the total. This makes analyses from different periods comparable. It should be

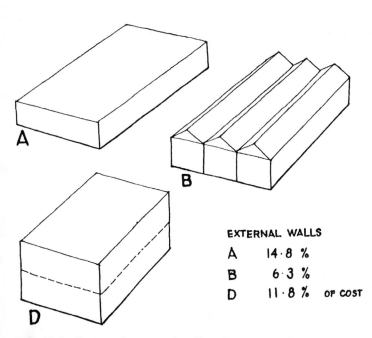

EXTERNAL WALLS

A   14·8 %

B   6·3 %

D   11·8 % OF COST

Fig. 12.1 Cost analyses can be directly compared

noted, however, that relative costs may change over a period of time and costs from more than say ten years ago should be treated with some reserve.

Cost plan

On the basis of several selected analyses for comparable buildings, and making due allowance for peculiarities of particular cases, such as difficult site conditions, or the omission of finishes to be completed by tenants, a cost plan for a projected building can be prepared. The full, sophisticated, plan will normally be drawn-up by a quantity surveyor, in cooperation with the architect, but a simple plan can be produced by the technician and form a useful guide in the early stages of work. Description of how this simpler operation can be done will serve to explain the principles involved.

Example

Small factory building

Consultation of published material might reveal five fairly recent jobs of roughly comparable type. They have been built over a period of

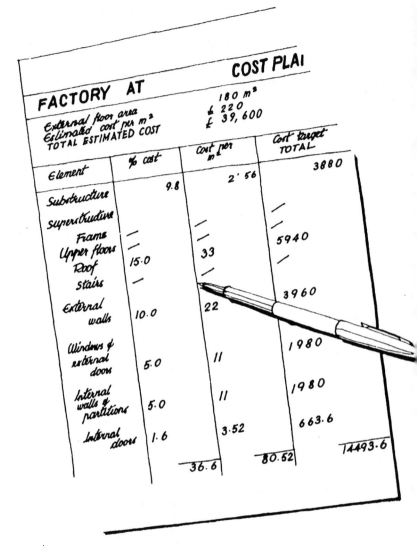

Fig. 12.2 Extract from cost plan

seven years, and the cost per square metre varies from £45 to £300, while floor area varies from 300 m² to 3 500 m². Not all are fully finished, two being intended for letting, while one is a very fully equipped and specialised workshop.

A is a single-storey brick building, with a high level of finishes, and a tight site.

B has no finishes and minimal services, and is a single-storey building with a steel frame.

C has wells of blockwork supporting light steel beams, and has the
  ancillary accommodation separately expressed under a low roof.
D is a high single-storey shell, within which two-storey offices have
  been incorporated.
E is a single-storey structure with a timber roof and brick walls, and
  has a very high level of services.
In order to make meaningful comparisons, the costs per element have
to be expressed as percentages of total cost.

Summary of cost analyses

Element groups	A	B	C	D	E	Proposed cost plan
Substructure	13.5	22.4	11.3	10.0	9.4	11.50
Superstructure	40.5	41.5	39.4	43.9	37.3	40.50
Internal finishes	10.5	0.5	4.3	8.9	3.6	5.50
Fittings and furniture	3.5	–	0.3	0.2	0.3	2.50
Services	18.4	4.4	21.4	16.6	33.8	19.00
External works	13.6	31.2	23.3	20.4	15.6	21.00
Total	100.0	100.0	100.0	100.0	100.0	100.00

(*preliminaries distributed*)

Note that most of the element groups given above are normally
broken-down further, and some examples of actual element costs for
these buildings are given below:

Roof	6.9	13.6	13.3	7.5	12.1
External walls	14.8	6.3	7.6	5.5	11.8
Electrical installation	6.1	0.4	5.8	5.0	7.6
Site work	1.6	15.9	12.1	11.7	12.7

Comparison of the five summaries immediately reveals some
anomalies, and these have to be taken into account when deciding
what the appropriate percentages to enter in the cost plan should be.

The figure for substructure at B is clearly unusually high, and
study of the scheme shows that this is a building on a particularly
difficult site. Since no particular problems are anticipated in this
respect, this figure should be ignored. The average of the four
remaining figures is 11.05

There are no obvious anomalies among the figures for superstructure, and it is noted that each of the forms of construction discussed in Chapter 8 is represented. The average figure is 40.52

The level of internal finishes is clearly very high in scheme A and very low in scheme B, so it is reasonable to ignore these figures and average the others at 5.6

The level of fittings in the project may be higher than in the speculative factories among the sample. The average figure of which may desirably be increased. It is 1.1

Scheme B includes virtually no services provision, while the level in E is very high due to the nature of the product. These schemes are ignored, and the average of the remaining figures is 18.8

The average expenditure on external works is 20.82

The total of these figures is 97.89
    leaving a remainder to be treated as contingencies or
    distributed, of 2.11
                                                                    ———
                                                                   100.00

    These figures would in all probability be rounded off, in the light of the expected conditions of the project, and such rounded figures have been filled-in in the chart on page 207.
    These figures do not, of course, comprise a whole cost plan. Further breakdown into cost targets for thirty or so individual elements would normally follow, working along similar lines with some back checking to ensure that no unrealistic targets were being set.
    In the light of the known overall cost limit, a simple calculation would show how much money was available in each case.
    During design, it will, of course, always be possible to adjust these figures, provided that if extra allowance has to be made (say) for the cost of the roof, because perhaps a high proportion of roof lights is needed, the allowance made for some other element must be adjusted down accordingly. The designer would probably endeavour to make the saving to some other element in the superstructure group (perhaps by reducing the allowance for external walls). Note that a reduction of 0.1 per cent will be much more serious if it is made on fittings than if it is made on external works – the most effective savings are to be made on structural items.
    Regular monitoring will now allow the quantity surveyor to advise on whether a particular potential detail can be afforded, or alternatively to give an idea of a number of options that might be financially open. ·
    If what is required costs too much, an informed decision can be

taken as to where the necessary saving should be made, while if a saving seems likely, the 'money' can be redistributed or added to a design contingency fund. Note that this fund is not intended to represent the contingency sum to be included in the bill, but is for future design contingencies that might arise.

Other estimating tools

At one time, costs were sufficiently stable for architects to understand with some precision what level of quality was implied by a particular cost per cubic foot or cost per square foot (this was before the days of metrication). It is no doubt possible that such conditions might return, but though at present it is helpful to be told how much per square metre a building has cost this is by no means the precise tool it once was.

One factor which it is very difficult to allow for is the contractor's attitude to the job. He tends to feel he must allow for possible difficulties and inflation which might occur – and prices go up. Most contracts today are subject to a fluctuation clause, so that the risk of inflation is removed so far as the builder is concerned. This means, however, that the client has to estimate the likely rise in costs due to inflation in budgeting for the job, and he may decide on a more modest building than he would wish for, if he could be sure of the eventual price.

Another factor which tends to raise prices unnecessarily is that the builder has to tender on the basis of a bill and outline drawings in most cases. He has, in fact, a very short period not only to price the bill, but also to work out how he will approach the job if he is successful, and to identify potential difficulties. He knows that if he overlooks something, he will nonetheless be deemed to have included for it in his tender. Will he, therefore, always expect and price for the worst? There is little incentive for the architect to design an easily constructed building, if there will be no financial advantage.

Terotechnology

For many years it was the practice to consider the capital cost of buildings quite separately from the cost of maintenance later. It almost seemed that the money involved was of two different kinds (indeed, an economist might argue that this was the case – that capital and revenue are so distinct that the separation is justified). Many buildings were designed so that they could be built as cheaply as possible, but with little or no consideration of the cost and inconvenience of upkeep and replacements.

210

The idea of terotechnology – first applied to the provision of industrial plant, but of much wider potential application – is to do away with that anomaly. Designers, and those who commission buildings, should take into account not only the initial outlay but the 'life-cycle' costs of what they buy.

If a building, or any other capital item, has a predicted life of forty years, the calculation will include interest charges on any loan (or loss of interest on money that could otherwise have been invested) the costs of replacement of parts at predicted intervals, the expense of regular maintenance (including wages and materials) insurances and any eventual resale value.

This is, of course, the way in which many people would approach the purchase of a car: they would cost the expense of running one they were considering per mile, including in their calculations depreciation, garaging, insurances, replacements and so on. It is an equally logical approach to the costing of buildings, and appears revolutionary only because maintenance and replacement costs have been ignored by designers for so long.

The effect can often be to show that the component or system which is apparently most expensive is actually a more economical choice when life-cycle costs are taken into account. Such calculations would be done for sophisticated equipment like lifts or cladding, but are equally applicable to simple components, and a simple example will explain the mechanism. Students should not let this very simplified example delude them into the belief that all such calculations are easy! (Fig. 12.3.)

Two floor finishes might be compared, for a building with a predicted life of sixty years.

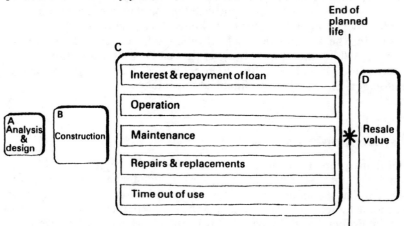

Life – cycle cost = cost of A + B + C – D

Fig. 12.3 Terotechnology is good housekeeping. Why cheesepare on first costs if the life-cycle costs will be astronomical?

Carpet at £15/m² needing to be replaced every six years and costing 5p/m² per week to vacuum clean and 10p/m² every six months to shampoo, would cost:
£(15 × 10) + (2.6 × 60) + (60 × 20) = £(150 + 156 + 120) = £426/m² over its life whereas a cushioned vinyl at £4/m² needing to be replaced every ten years and costing 10p/m² per day to wash, would cost £(4 × 6) + (35.6 × 60) = £(24 + 2 136) = £2 160/m² in the same period.
Obviously, there might be functional reasons for choosing the dearer alternative, but the cost of doing so should be understood.

Cheap and expensive building

Some forms of building are by their nature more expensive than others, without providing any particular advantage in exchange for the extra expenditure. They can be avoided if one is aware of them – and if they are in fact adopted, this should be done for good reasons and with one's eyes open.
Some of the rules are noted below.

1. A compact building tends to be cheaper than a sprawling one. It is cheaper to enclose as much volume as possible in as small an envelope as can be managed. A cube is ideal.
2. Unnecessary space should not be enclosed. The plan should be carefully devised to be as compact as possible. This is also likely to produce a more convenient building.
3. Changes of roof level are expensive, and so are hips and valleys (Fig. 12.4).

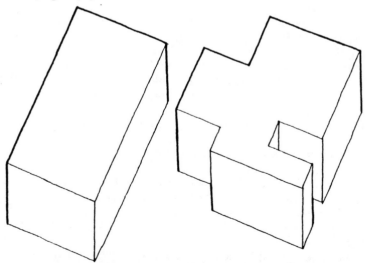

Fig. 12.4 Significant financial savings can be made by adopting a simple structure

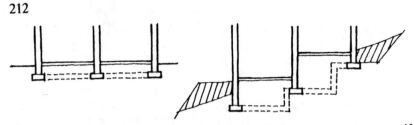

Fig. 12.5 Expensive foundations that are buried are an extravagance if possible they should be avoided.

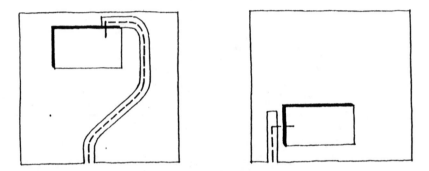

Fig. 12.6 Why spend money on expensive roads and service runs if it could be saved by siting the building differently?

4. Buildings that follow the contours avoid the need for elaborate foundations, and often for suspended floors.
5. Cut and fill should be balanced as far as possible, in exploiting the site (Fig. 12.5).
6. It is easier to save money by choosing a simple structure than by cheeseparing finishes.
7. Having chosen a structure, it will be cheapest to use beams at their maximum span, lintols at maximum load and so on.
8. Nothing should be put in the building unless it is known to be useful. Be sure you know why every mould and cover strip is there.
9. Repetition, other things being equal, is cheaper than needless variety.
10. Natural finishes which look good and need little maintenance can often be relatively cheap.
11. Short roads and service runs, and drains that run with the contours so as to stay shallow, have obvious advantages. (Fig. 12.6)
12. Grass is the cheapest ground cover.
13. Trees, especially existing full-grown ones, are cheap and effective features on any site.
    It is, of course, impossible to list all the devices which might save

money. What is necessary is that the design team always demand value for what is spent, and take a critical look from that point of view at all they choose. The architectural technician may often find he is being asked to provide cost information – he should never assume he is simply being asked to find the cheapest available expedient.

Chapter 13

Legal restraints

Introduction

Although the amount of restriction put upon building and the people
involved in it may seem onerous at times, it is difficult to see how the
extent of the control exercised could be much reduced. If a building
was going to be used only by the people who built it, was invisible to
the outside world, used no resources, needed no services and caused
no obstruction or potential danger, then there might be an arguable
case for letting a man build what he liked. As it is, of course, buildings
are used by the public, they are adjacent to public roads, they might
collapse or obstruct other buildings, and they make an important
contribution, for good or ill, to the visual environment. In these
circumstances it is only reasonable that those who perpetrate them
should have to submit to control for the general good of the
community.

The law protects the rights of the owners of adjacent property, it
ensures that acceptable standards of health and safety are reached and
it controls the way in which resources especially those of land and of
the environment, are used.

Every community finds it necessary to legislate about such matters.
A free-for-all results in shanty towns and land rushes, and it is only
cooperation between owners (and their agents) who sometimes have to
sacrifice freedom to the consensus view, that leads to the creation of a
safe and attractive built environment.

English law is a complex subject, and always developing. A

solicitor should always be consulted in any area where doubt or dispute arises, and it is only a solicitor who has the professional expertise to search out titles to land and do conveyancing – especially of unregistered sites.

Most contracts are made without reference to a solicitor. There is no objection to this if the matter is simple and quickly completed, or if a standard form is used. Litigation is the all too common result of more elaborate 'do-it-yourself' contracts.

Legal language is traditionally dry and precise for the good reason that it attempts to avoid ambiguity. This is something most laymen (non-lawyers, that is) find hard to achieve.

This chapter is no more than a brief and general introduction to the main areas of the law governing building work. None of the 'definitions' included in it is any more than a simple layman's explanation of the term in question. Some words will be found to have been used in their common rather than their legal sense. The law in Scotland is in many instances different from ,hat in England and Wales, and what is said in this chapter may not apply to Scotland.

Ownership of land

For every piece of land there is a freeholder, who is someone who is for every practical purpose the 'owner' of it. He can sell it, give it away, or leave it to someone in his will, and he has a 'title' or certificate that no one else has a better right to it than he has.

He probably can't do just as he likes, unfettered, with his land, however. He may, for example, lease the land to a tenant for any period they agree upon, and (subject to the terms of the lease) many of the rights of ownership will pass to the leaseholder. The lease is secure unless one party or the other contravenes its conditions.

It is common for building land to be leased to a developer, so that houses or other buildings can be built upon it and the leases of the individual properties then sold to individuals. The buildings commonly revert to the ownership of the freeholder at the end of the agreed period, and freeholders often reserve the right of control over what is built and how it is used and maintained. This has the advantage of preserving an estate intact, of avoiding decline and allowing eventual comprehensive redevelopment. It is to the advantage of householders that they now have the right to purchase their freeholds in certain circumstances, but it may mean the end of some well preserved residential suburbs. The alternative method of conserving such areas is available under the Town and Country Planning Acts (see below).

Both freeholders and leaseholders may find that their absolute right to use their property as they wish is modified not only by statute, but also by the overriding rights of others. The most important of these are easements.

216

Easements

Easements are rights which the owner or occupier of one piece of land may acquire over the land of another. The two properties must be joining and must be in different ownerships. One owner must have an advantage at the expense of some inconvenience to the other. It must be possible to make an actual grant of the right, which means among other things that it must be possible to define it. The right to privacy, to a view, or to a flow of air do not fall into this definition, but the most important easements are the right to light, the right of way and the right of support to buildings.

Easements may be granted by deed, but often arise because they have been enjoyed without interruption for a long period – twenty years is generally sufficient before an action was started, so long as the use was continuous. Some easements arise because they are implied – for example, if one sells a piece of land, and the only access to it is through one's back garden, a right of way would have been created by implication.

Easements are very difficult to extinguish, except by the two properties coming into the same ownership.

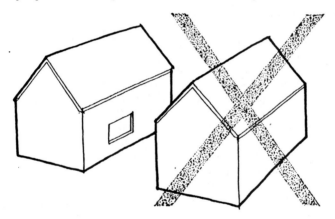

Fig. 13.1 Right of light

Right of light ('Ancient Lights')
The right is not a general one, but applies to a particular opening, and it isn't (as is often thought) a right to unrestricted light, but to the amount of light needed for ordinary purposes. The period needed to establish right of light was extended to twenty-seven years in 1959, to protect bomb-damaged buildings which had not yet been rebuilt from rights attached to newly unobstructed windows in adjacent buildings. At the same time, a mechanism was devised by which the owner of such a vacant site could be deemed (by giving notice or registering a right at the land registry) to have erected an obstructing hoarding.

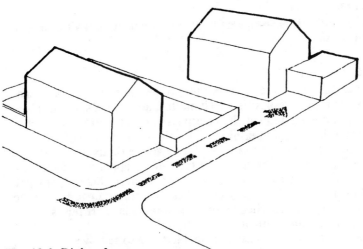

Fig. 13.2 Right of way

Right of way

Right of way may be limited to a footpath or bridleway, or to particular users, or may be enjoyed by the public. It can have a severe effect on the way in which a site can be developed. Many owners who admit the public regularly to their property (for example, householders in private roads, railway authorities) close the access on one day of each year to prevent acquisition of a right of way by continuous use.

Right of support

A building can acquire the right of support by its neighbour (for instance, if it is one of a terrace of houses) unless a written statement to the contrary is obtained. This is not the same thing as land itself being entitled to support from an adjoining site, which is established by 'long user'.

Land may be sold subject to a new easement, or reserving rights to the seller, or with covenants as to the use to which it is to be put.

A wayleave is a right for which a rent (often a peppercorn rent) is paid, such as the right of an electricity board to run cables over a site. It is less difficult to extinguish than an easement: the subservient owner can simply terminate the agreement (according to its terms). It is not necessary for the dominant owner to own adjoining property.

Certain rights to clean water, and an unobstructed flow of water from a stream, to take fish and so on can also be defined.

Rents, mortgages and land tax

These are further ways in which the rights of owners may be modified.

Rights of entry

Many public officials have rights of entry to property, notwithstanding the law of trespass.

Trespass

Either a permanent or a temporary entry to another owner's land can constitute trespass. Trespass is a civil matter, and one is sued, not prosecuted, if one commits it. It is trespass to erect scaffolding on a neighbouring site without permission, for the maintenance of a building unless (as is sometimes the case) owner's rights to this effect have been preserved. If this is so, the fact will be apparent from the title deeds. It is also trespass to make a mistake in setting out, and get the building a few centimetres over the site boundary, or to let a fence be put up where it encroaches on the neighbour's land. If this is unnoticed, an easement might be established.

An owner is entitled to use reasonable force to remove trespassers, but not to take a shotgun to them – though he will not be responsible for any accidental injury they encounter, as he is in the case of visitors he invites or lets in unobstructed. In the case of building sites, this means that if the agent knows a visitor is on-site, and doesn't object, he will be responsible if there is an accident, but if uninvited visitors appear, he will not. All visitors to site, for this reason, should always make their presence known on arrival, and follow any directions intended to protect them, such as the wearing of hard hats or careful use of ladders.

Nuisance

Anything which stops an owner from enjoying his property reasonably constitutes a nuisance. Someone who buys a house on a busy street cannot then claim that the traffic is a nuisance (although it may be very annoying) because that is a reasonable thing to have to put up with in a house in that situation. If a sawmill starts up next door, that might be thought unreasonable, and therefore actionable. Noise, smells, smoke, heat might all constitute a nuisance, depending on what was reasonable in the circumstances.

There is a difficulty. An injunction might be obtained subject to appeal. If the appeal was won, the party who took the action might find himself liable to damages for the lost profit of a business that couldn't trade pending the hearing.

Building regulations

The Building Regulations are largely concerned with the safety of buildings and their occupants. Thus the provision of a clean water supply, good drains, adequate ventilation and fireproof chimneys is very much their affair, as well as the stability of structures and the design of foundations, and so on.

On the whole, the Regulations set standards to be achieved, and describe a number of strategies, the adoption of any one of which would be deemed to satisfy the requirement. There is nothing to prevent an applicant from proposing some alternative means of doing so, providing he can establish that his proposals will fully meet the standards laid down. This has the advantage over the old-style byelaws of encouraging innovation.

The Regulations are subject to continuous revision, and respond to the developing experience of the industry. They should be seen as encapsulating the collected wisdom of the industry for everyone's advantage rather than providing undesirable restraints.

The Building Regulations are administered by county and metropolitan district councils, though the former delegate many powers to the districts. The latter should usually be approached in the first instance.

The officials who administer the regulations are mostly pleased to be consulted on the interpretation of them, though they naturally cannot be expected to redesign unsatisfactory proposals for applicants. Deposited plans are kept, but can often only be consulted by the owner of the property or his authorised representative, for copyright reasons.

It is an offence to commence without first applying for permission, and work done under such conditions is liable to be dismantled. Work must also be left open for inspection at stated stages.

London

The London Building Acts control these aspects of building in the capital, and may be quite different in their effect from the Regulations. They are administered by London boroughs.

Town and country planning

Planning controls are intended to ensure that the land available is used responsibly for the good of the community. Its most important feature from this point of view is the 'zoning' of land to limit the purposes for which it can be used.

Local plans are prepared, which indicate the proposed zonings for the various sites, as well as the way in which transport and other services will be provided. There may be presumptions in favour of particular uses, even within the categories zoned, and all owners who intend to develop their property have to apply for permission to do so, so that their ideas can be compared to the adopted plan.

Development includes not only building work and other actual alterations to the land and what is on it (such as quarrying) but also a change of use of the land which could occur without any physical change at all. If a field was to stop being used to graze cows, in order to be used as a car park, or a house was to be used as offices or a warehouse, in each case this would constitute development, and planning permission would be needed. On the other hand, there are some categories of actual alterations to property, particularly internal alterations and small extensions, which are exempt from planning rules, though they still require approval under the Building Regulations.

Permission can be sought in a general way for a particular proposed use of land (outline permission) in which case approval of detailed proposals (reserved matters) has to be obtained later. Outline permission can be obtained by someone who doesn't own the property, such as a prospective purchaser, provided he tells the owner what he is doing.

There is an elaborate machinery to allow the public to participate in the planning process, and to object to development that would have an adverse effect on their interests.

Houses and trees can be made subject to preservation orders, severely limiting what can be done to them, and whole districts can be made into conservation areas, to preserve their character.

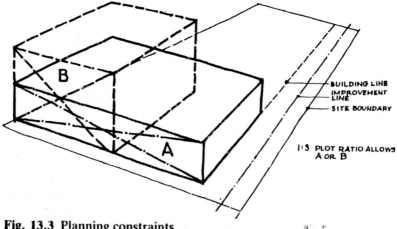

Fig. 13.3 Planning constraints

Besides controlling the type of use that can be made of land, planning also controls the materials used, appearance, heights, densities and space around buildings. In conservation areas, this control is much more stringent. The aim is to maintain an area that is believed to have a special character, not to preserve every existing feature of it.

Planning is administered by local authorities on behalf of central government, and it is possible to appeal against decisions to the Department of the Environment.

Guidance on making applications and appeals can be obtained from the planning department of a county council or metropolitan district council.

Work must not, of course, be started until permission has been granted, and must take account of any conditions approval includes.

Health and safety

The builder has a responsibility to his workpeople to maintain the conditions in which they work to defined standards, especially of safety. The architect, too, may need to consult the detailed provisions of the Act if he is designing office or factory premises as well as in connection with the workplaces he provides for his own staff.

Contracts

A contract exists whenever one person offers to supply goods or services in return for a 'consideration' (usually money) and the other party agrees. Most contracts are invalidated if either of these terms is subsequently altered, but fortunately this is specifically not true of a building contract.

All contracts must be able to be proved to exist, and there must be no doubt as to what the conditions are. For anything so elaborate it will, therefore, almost inevitably have to be in writing. The easiest, as well as the safest, option is to use whichever of the standard forms of contract (prepared by the Joint Contracts Tribunal representing the professional bodies of the industry) is most applicable to the case.

These forms, as well as having been most carefully evolved over many years, have been exhaustively tested by the courts, and are widely and precisely understood. They are complicated because they have been carefully drawn-up to cover virtually every contingency that might arise. This means that if either party dies or goes bankrupt, or the half-finished building is demolished by a bomb, or a vital material trebles in price, the procedure to be adopted has already been agreed, and if there should be a dispute that the architect couldn't resolve, arrangements for arbitration are available.

The architect is not a party to the contract, but has a defined position under it.

Suppliers

The statutory undertakers who supply essential services such as water and gas publish byelaws which must be understood and complied with. There are two reasons for this.

1. Compatibility. Clearly standardisation is essential if an efficient service is to be provided.
2. Safety. The undertaker has a continually growing body of knowledge of safe and efficient ways of using his service, and the byelaws ensure that the advantages of the latest safety standards are available to the public.

Undertakers usually refuse to connect services unless installations in buildings comply with their requirements.

Airports

There may be special requirements governing building in the vicinity of airports, affecting heights and also the provision of sound insulation.

Insurers

It is common for insurers to demand particular standards of fire resistance or locks (for example) before they will provide cover for buildings. The alternative may be prohibitively high premiums. The advice insurance companies can provide is expert and valuable, and well worth obtaining for any building where special security problems are anticipated.

Fire prevention

The fire prevention officer is available in any area to give advice on safety in the design of buildings, and usually works closely with the building inspector. He can discuss means of escape and of fire-fighting, including both the installation of hose reels, extinguishers and so on and the provision of access for the brigade. Although it is not mandatory to follow his advice, it would presumably be evidence of professional negligence if an architect failed to do so.

Special regulations control the arrangements for fire prevention and escape in hotels.

Conditions of engagement

Standardised conditions of engagement control the relationships of all members of professional bodies in building design with their clients. Though the details vary, and are of course subject to amendment from time to time, they are all based on the principle of providing a service in exchange for a fee. Great care is taken to avoid any suggestion of a clash of loyalties or a commercial interest in the project, so that the client can entirely rely on his advisers representing his own interests and giving him disinterested advice.

This standard extends to employees, and technicians should obtain and study the Conditions of Engagement published by the Royal Institute of British Architects, 66 Portland Place, London WIN 4AD.

Professionals act as agents for their clients, which means they have wide but defined powers to act on their behalf.

Code of conduct

The conditions referred to above are complemented by codes of professional conduct which determine relationships also with the public and professional colleagues. Professionals who contravene the relevant code may even lose the right to practice. Employees' actions are attributable to their employers.

Architectural technicians should be familiar with the codes of the RIBA and the Architects Registration Councils 'Conduct and Discipline'.

Negligence

Negligence is a failure to exercise reasonable care or skill, where the person concerned has a duty to do so, as an architect has to his client. 'Reasonable' is difficult to determine, but certainly does not mean exceptional skill. A person practising professionally is expected to maintain a competent standard, and this might be judged by comparison with what colleagues in the profession would be likely to do in the same circumstances.

Employers are liable for negligence by their salaried staff.

Index